COUNTY FERM...
100 YEARS ...

PUBLISHER'S NOTE

This volume contains a reprint of *Lowe's Fermanagh directory and household almanac for 1880*. This edition has been given the title *County Fermanagh 100 years ago: a guide and directory, 1880*.

Acknowledgement is made to the Fermanagh Divisional Library for the use of its copy of *Lowe's Fermanagh directory and household almanac for 1880*.

This edition, 1990, Friar's Bush Press, 24 College Park Avenue, Belfast BT7 1LR.
Cover illustration *Enniskillen from Portora Hill, 1874* taken from *Enniskillen long ago* by W. H. Bradshaw (Dublin 1878, reissue 1892).
Cover design and printing by W. & G. Baird Ltd., Antrim.
ISBN 0 946872 29 5

COUNTY FERMANAGH
100 YEARS AGO

a guide and directory
1880

by
HENRY N. LOWE

The Friar's Bush Press

LOWE'S

FERMANAGH DIRECTORY

AND

Household Almanac

FOR 1880,

BEING BISSEXTILE, OR LEAP YEAR.

CHRONOLOGICAL CYCLES, 1880.

Dominical Letters, D C.—Solar Cycle, 13.—Golden Number, 19.—Epact, 18.—
Roman Indiction, 8.—Julian Period, 6593.

FIXED AND MOVEABLE FESTIVALS, 1880.

Epiphany	Jan. 6	Pentecost—Whit Sunday	May	16
Septuagesima Sunday	,, 25	Trinity Sunday	,,	23
Quinqua.—Shrove Sunday	Feb. 8	Birth of Queen Victoria	,,	24
Ash Wednesday	,, 11	Corpus Christi	,,	27
Quadra.—1st Sunday in Lent	,, 15	Accession of Queen Victoria	June 20
St. David	Mar. 1	Proclamation Day	,,	21
St. Patrick's Day	,, 17	St. John Baptist—Midsummer	
Palm Sunday	,, 21	Day	,,	24
Annunciation—Lady Day	,, 25	St. Michael—Michaelmas Day Sep. 29
Good Friday	,, 26	Birth of Prince of Wales	Nov. 9
Easter Sunday	,, 28	1st Sunday in Advent	,,	28
Low Sunday	April 4	St. Andrew's Day	,,	30
St. George	,, 23	St. Thomas's Day	Dec. 21
Rogation Sunday	May 2	Christmas Day	,,	25
Ascen Day—Holy Thursday	,, 6	St. John s Day	,,	27

The year 5641 of the Jewish Era commences on 6th September, 1880.

Ramadán (Month of Abstinence observed by the Turks) commences on 7th August, 1880.

The year 1298 of the Mohammedan Era commences on 4th December, 1880.

ECLIPSES, 1880.

In the year 1880 there will be four Eclipses of the Sun and two of the Moon:—

January 11.—Total Eclipse of the Sun, invisible at Greenwich.
July 6, 7.—An Annular Eclipse of the Sun, invisible at Greenwich.
December 1.—A Partial Eclipse of the Sun, invisible at Greenwich.
December 31.—A Partial Eclipse of the Sun, visible at Greenwich.
June 21, 22.—A Total Eclipse of the Moon, invisible at Greenwich.
December 16.—A Total Eclipse of the Moon, partly visible at Greenw

January.

Days Month	Days Week	THE SUN		THE MOON					High Water at Derry Quay.	
		Rises	Sets	Rises Aftern.	Sets Morn.	Age	Souths		Morn	Even
		H. M.	H. M.	H. M.	H. M.		H. M.		H. M.	H. M.
1	Thursday, ...	8 20	...	8 35	9 47	19	2	42	10 19	10 43
2	Friday, ...	...	3 42	9 48	10 3	20	3	27	11 4	11 28
3	Saturday ...	8 20	...	11 5	10 21	21	4	12	11 25	11 49
4	SUNDAY, ...	...	3 43	morn	10 37	22	4	58	0 10	0 35
5	Monday, ...	8 25	...	0 25	10 54	23	5	46	0 59	1 23
6	Tuesday, ...	...	3 47	1 45	11 15	24	6	36	1 49	2 13
7	Wednesday, ...	8 24	...	3 8	11 45	25	7	31	2 44	3 8
8	Thursday, ...	...	3 51	4 34	aftern	26	8	31	3 44	4 8
9	Friday, ...	8 23	...	5 52	1 13	27	9	34	4 47	5 11
10	Saturday, ...	...	3 54	6 58	2 23	28	10	39	5 49	6 16
11	SUNDAY, ...	8 21	...	7 46	3 42	N	11	41	6 54	7 18
12	Monday, ...	...	3 57	8 21	5 10	1	0a	41	8 18	8 42
13	Tuesday, ...	8 19	...	8 48	6 35	2	1	35	9 12	9 36
14	Wednesday, ...	...	4 0	9 6	7 55	3	2	25	10 2	10 26
15	Thursday, ...	8 17	...	9 24	9 13	4	3	12	10 37	11 13
16	Friday, ...	...	4 4	9 39	10 28	5	3	56	11 33	11 57
17	Saturday, ...	8 15	...	9 55	11 40	6	4	39	11 54	0 18
18	SUNDAY, ...	...	4 7	10 11	morn	7	5	23	0 36	1 0
19	Monday, ...	8 13	...	10 29	0 50	8	6	7	1 20	1 44
20	Tuesday, ...	...	4 12	10 51	1 59	9	6	53	2 6	2 30
21	Wednesday, ...	8 10	...	11 19	3 9	10	7	41	2 54	3 18
22	Thursday, ...	...	4 16	11 55	4 18	11	8	30	3 43	4 7
23	Friday, ...	8 7	...	aftern	5 11	12	9	21	4 34	4 58
24	Saturday, ...	...	4 19	1 38	5 59	13	10	11	5 24	5 48
25	SUNDAY, ...	8 4	...	2 41	6 38	14	11	2	6 15	6 39
26	Monday, ...	...	4 23	3 52	7 9	15	11	51	7 4	7 28
27	Tuesday, ...	8 1	...	5 6	7 35	F	morn		7 37	8 1
28	Wednesday, ...	...	4 27	6 21	7 54	17	0	39	8 16	8 40
29	Thursday, ...	7 58	...	7 38	8 12	18	1	25	9 2	9 26
30	Friday, ...	...	4 31	8 55	8 29	19	2	11	9 48	10 12
31	Saturday, ...	7 55	...	10 3	8 45	20	2	57	10 34	10 58

PHASES OF THE MOON.

Last Quarter, Monday, 5th day, at 49m. past 6, a.m.
New Moon, Sunday, 11th day, at 40m. past 10, p.m.
First Quarter, Monday, 19th day, at 40m. past 6, a.m.
Full Moon, Tuesday, 27th day, at 12m. past 10, a.m.

The hours of High Water at the Quays are shown in the Calendar for the several days. To find High Water at the Flats, deduct 1 hour and 30 minutes; and at the Lough, deduct 1 hour and 45 minutes.

BUSINESS REMEMBRANCER.

The *Registers of Births, Deaths, and Marriages* for the preceding three months must be sent during this month by the Registrars to the Superintendent Registrars, for transmission to the Registrar-General. 7 & 8 Vic., c. 81 ; 26 Vic., c. 11 & 27 ; and 26 & 27 Vic., c. 90.

Registration of Births & Deaths—Parents and others must give notice, within 21 days, to the Registrar of their district of the birth of any child born in Ireland ; and intimation of death to be given to the Registrar within 7 days. Penalty for failing to give notice, 20s. 26 Vic., c. 11.

Every Registrar of Births and Deaths is required, once in every month, to transmit to the Vaccination Officer of the place a return of the births and deaths of all infants under 12 months old which have been registered by him. 34 & 35 Vic., c. 98.

Vaccination.—Parents and Guardians of children must have such children vaccinated within 6 months after birth. 26 & 27 Vic., c. 52.

Public Houses.—Act 41 & 42 Vic., cap. 72, prohibits the sale of intoxicating liquors to the whole of Sunday in Ireland, except within the Metropolitan Police District of Dublin, and within the cities of Cork, Limerick, and Waterford, and the town of Belfast.

Loan Fund Trustees to transmit in this month, to Central Loan Fund Board, an Abstract of Accounts for preceding year, made up to 31st December. 6 & 7 Vic., c. 91.

1st. *Holiday* on Stock Exchange and Banks in Scotland.

1st. *Dividends* on Bank of Ireland Stock payable.

1st. *Returns of Partners in all Banks in Ireland* to be made to the Stamp Office in Dublin : penalty for omission, £50. 8 & 9 Vic., c. 37.

1st. *Property and Income Tax* for year ending 5th April, 1880, due and payable in one sum. 32 & 33 Vic., c. 14, s. 8.

9th. *Fire Insurance* Premium due at Christmas must be paid by this day, or the Policy becomes void.

10th. *Borough Coroners* to transmit to Lord Lieutenant a return of Inquests held in year preceding. 3 & 4 Vic., c. 108.

19th. Last day for making out and issuing *Half-yearly Receipts for Interest* to Savings Banks and Friendly Societies. 7 & 8 Vic., c. 83.

31st. *Annual Account of Receipts and Expenditure of Commissioners under Towns Improvement Act* to be transmitted to Clerk of Peace of the County, on or before 31st January, or within a month after audit, under a penalty of £20 on the Commissioners.

31st. *Gas Companies*, on or before 31st January in each year, to prepare abstract of receipts and expenditure of all rents or funds levied for the year preceding, with a statement of balance of such account audited and certified by the chairman or auditors ; a copy of such account to be forwarded to Clerk of the Peace for county in which gasworks are situated. 10 Vic., c. 15.

MISTRESSES would not so often be afraid of speaking the truth about their servants if they knew (1) that a mistress is not bound to give a servant a character ; (2) that when a mistress gives a discharged servant a character, what she says or writes upon the subject to a person *bona-fide* inquiring is in general looked upon as a privileged communication, and no action can be maintained on account of it, if done *bona-fide* and without malice.

February.

Days Month	Days Week	THE SUN		THE MOON				High Water at Ferry Quay.	
		Rises	Sets	Rises Aftern.	Sets Morn.	Age	Souths	Morn	Even
		H M	H M	H M	H M		H M	H M	H M
1	Sunday,	7 53	...	11 32	9 2	21	3 44	11 24	11 45
2	Monday,	...	4 37	morn	9 22	22	4 33	11 46	0 10
3	Tuesday,	7 50	...	0 55	9 4	23	5 26	0 39	1 3
4	Wednesday,	...	4 41	2 18	10 19	24	6 22	1 35	1 59
5	Thursday,	7 46	...	3 36	11 5	25	7 22	2 35	2 59
6	Friday,	...	4 45	4 45	aftern	26	8 24	3 37	4 1
7	Saturday,	7 42	...	5 38	1 19	27	9 2	4 39	5 3
8	Sunday,	...	4 49	6 17	2 40	28	10 25	5 38	6 2
9	Monday,	7 37	...	6 48	4 5	29	11 21	6 34	6 58
10	Tuesday,	...	4 55	7 11	5 28	N	0a 12	7 49	8 13
11	Wednesday,	7 33	...	7 28	6 48	1	1 1	8 38	9 2
12	Thursday,	...	4 49	7 44	8 4	2	1 47	9 24	9 48
13	Friday,	7 29	...	8 0	9 18	3	2 31	10 8	10 32
14	Saturday,	...	5 3	8 17	10 30	4	3 16	10 41	11 17
15	Sunday,	7 25	...	8 33	11 42	5	4 1	11 14	11 38
16	Monday,	...	5 7	8 55	morn	6	4 46	0 3	0 27
17	Tuesday,	7 21	...	9 20	0 52	7	5 33	0 46	1 10
18	Wednesday,	...	5 11	9 52	1 58	8	6 22	1 35	1 59
19	Thursday,	7 17	...	10 32	2 59	9	7 12	2 25	2 49
20	Friday,	...	5 15	11 32	3 52	10	8 2	3 15	3 39
21	Saturday,	7 12	...	aftern	4 35	11	8 53	4 6	4 30
22	Sunday,	...	5 19	1 34	5 9	12	9 42	4 55	5 19
23	Monday,	7 7	...	2 46	5 36	13	10 31	5 45	6 9
24	Tuesday	...	5 23	4 3	5 58	14	11 18	6 31	6 55
25	Wednesday,	7 2	...	5 19	6 17	15	11 41	6 55	7 19
26	Thursday,	...	5 27	6 36	6 35	F	morn	7 37	8 1
27	Friday,	6 58	...	7 57	6 51	17	0 52	8 29	8 53
28	Saturday,	...	5 32	9 10	7 8	18	1 40	9 17	9 41
29	Sunday,	6 54	...	10 41	7 28	19	2 30	10 6	10 30

PHASES OF THE MOON.

Last Quarter, Tuesday, 3rd day, at 38m. past 3, p.m.
New Moon, Tuesday, 10th day, at 17m. past 11, a.m.
First Quarter, Wednesday, 18th day, at 46m. past 3, a.m.
Full Moon, Thursday, 26th day, at 22m. past 1, a.m.

BUSINESS REMEMBRANCER.

In this month *Half-Yearly* Return of Transfers, &c., to be made to the Registrar of Joint Stock Companies, by every Company *completely* registered under Act, and not afterwards incorporated. 7 & 8 Vic., c. 110. *Annual* Return of Name and Business of every such Company to be made also in this month.—*Ib.*

Guardians of the Poor—In this month, notice for the Election of Guardians of the Poor will be issued by the Returning Officer for each Union. Landlords who have not claimed to vote *in respect of rent payable to them*, and Clergymen or Impropriators who have not claimed to vote in respect of tithe rent-charge, also Occupiers liable to rents *under the net annual value* of their tenements, who have not claimed to vote in respect of the beneficial interests so possessed, should send in statements of their claims to the Board of Guardians of the Union on or before the 18th of this month. Landlords entitled to vote in respect of rents received, and owners of tithe rent-charge, may also appoint Proxies to vote for them. Suitable forms for these several purposes can be seen at the office of the Clerk of each Union.

1st. *Shooting Pheasants* prohibited from this date to the 1st October. 28 & 29 Vic., c. 54.

1st. *Angling*, with single rod and line, in rivers frequented by salmon, permitted from this date to 30th October. 26 & 27 Vic., c. 114.

1st. *Accounts of Borough Income and Expenditure* for preceding year to be transmitted to Lord Lieutenant by Town Councils, Commissioners, or Boards of Guardians of the Poor, in whichever the property shall have been vested. 3 & 4 Vic., c. 108.

2nd. *Heath, Furze, &c.*, not to be burned on mountains, &c. (save on parts broken up for agriculture or planting), between this date and 14th June following: penalty, £5. 10 Wm. III., c. 8; and 27 Geo. III., c. 35.

6th. Last day for *Solicitors* taking out their certificates to practise in 1880.

15th. *Wild fowl* are not to be taken or killed between this day and 10th of July. Penalty, 20s for every wild fowl killed, wounded, or taken, or in possession of any person. 39 & 40 Vic., c. 29.

18th. Last day for *Receiving Owners' Statements of Claims to Vote in the Election of Poor-Law Guardians*, voting papers being issued on the 18th of March.

27th. *Railway Companies* to furnish accounts to Board of Trade.

SOMETHING WORTH KNOWING.—Every little while we read in the papers of some one who has stuck a rusty nail in his foot, or knee, hand, or some other portion of his body, and that lock-jaw resulted therefrom, of which the patient died. If every person was aware of a perfect remedy for all such wounds, and apply it, then all such reports would cease. But although we can give the remedy, we cannot enforce the application. The remedy is simple, almost always on hand, and can be applied by anyone, and what is better, it is infallible. It is simply to smoke the wound, or any bruise or wound that is inflamed, with burning wool or woollen cloth. Twenty minutes in the smoke of wool will take the pain out of the worst wound; repeated two or three times, it will allay the worst cases of inflammation arising from a wound. People may sneer at "the old man's remedy" as much as they please, but when they are afflicted just let them try it. It has saved many lives and much pain, and is worthy of being printed in letters of gold and put in every home.—*Home Surgery.*

Days Month	Days Week	THE SUN		THE MOON				High Water at Derry Quay.	
		Rises	Sets	Rises Morn.	Sets Morn.	Age	Souths	Morn	Even
		H M	H M	H M	H M		H M	H M	H M
1	Monday, ...	6 52	...	...	7 52 20	3	22	10 59	11 23
2	Tuesday, ...	...	5 35	0 5	8 23 21	4	18	11 31	11 55
3	Wednesday, ...	6 49	...	1 26	9 5 22	5	17	0 30	0 54
4	Thursday, ...	...	5 39	2 36	9 59 23	6	17	1 30	1 54
5	Friday, ...	6 44	...	3 33	11 7 24	7	18	2 31	2 55
6	Saturday, ...	..	5 43	4 17	aftern 25	8	17	3 30	3 54
7	SUNDAY, ...	6 38	...	4 49	1 45 26	9	12	4 25	4 49
8	Monday, ...	...	5 47	5 13	3 5 27	10	3	5 16	5 40
9	Tuesday, ...	6 33	...	5 34	4 26 28	10	52	6 5	6 29
10	Wednesday, ...	...	5 51	5 50	5 42 29	11	39	6 52	7 16
11	Thursday, ...	6 28	...	6 6	6 56 N	0a	24	8 1	8 25
12	Friday, ...	...	5 56	6 22	8 11 1	1	8	8 45	9 9
13	Saturday, ...	6 22	...	6 38	9 23 2	1	53	9 30	9 54
14	SUNDAY, ...	...	6 0	6 59	10 35 3	2	39	10 16	10 40
15	Monday, ...	6 17	...	7 22	11 43 4	3	26	11 3	11 27
16	Tuesday, ...	...	6 4	7 5	morn 5	4	14	11 27	11 51
17	Wednesday, ...	6 12	...	8 30	0 45 6	5	4	0 4	0 28
18	Thursday, ...	...	6 7	9 16	1 42 7	5	53	1 6	1 30
19	Friday, ...	6 7	...	10 12	2 28 8	6	43	1 56	2 20
20	Saturday, ...	...	6 11	11 17	3 5 9	7	32	2 45	3 9
21	SUNDAY, ...	6 3	...	aftern	3 36 10	8	21	3 34	3 58
22	Monday, ...	...	6 15	1 39	4 1 11	9	8	4 21	4 45
23	Tuesday, ...	5 57	...	2 54	4 21 12	9	55	5 6	5 30
24	Wednesday, ...	...	6 19	4 13	4 40 13	10	42	5 55	6 19
25	Thursday, ...	5 52	...	5 33	4 56 14	11	39	6 52	7 16
26	Friday, ...	...	6 22	6 55	5 12 F	morn		7 37	8 1
27	Saturday, ...	5 47	...	8 19	5 32 16	0	20	7 57	8 21
28	SUNDAY, ...	...	6 26	9 35	5 55 17	1	13	8 50	9 14
29	Monday, ...	5 43	...	11 8	6 26 18	2	10	9 47	10 11
30	Tuesday, ...	...	6 30	morn	7 3 19	3	9	10 46	11 10
31	Wednesday, ...	5 38	...	0 25	7 56 20	4	11	11 24	11 48

PHASES OF THE MOON.

Last Quarter, Wednesday, 3rd day, at 6m. past 11, p.m.
New Moon, Thursday, 11th day, at 47m. past 12, p.m.
First Quarter, Friday, 19th day, at 36m. past 12, p.m.
Full Moon, Friday, 26th day, at 23m. past 1, p.m.

BUSINESS REMEMBRANCER.

1st. Copies of *Returns of Partners in Banks in Ireland* to be published in the *Dublin Gazette*, by Commissioners of Stamps. 8 & 9 Vic., c. 37.

1st. *Close season* for oysters in Carlingford Lough, 1st March to 1st November.

25th. *Appointments of Public Officers and Enrolments of Admissions to Corporations*—not provided, or which have been lost or mislaid—may be provided, duly stamped, on or before this day; and unstamped appointments or admissions may be stamped on payment of double the original duty. 7 Vic., c 10.

25th. *Freemasons' Societies and Friendly Brothers* to register name of Society, place and time of meeting, and names and description of Members, with the Clerk of the Peace for the County, annually, on or before this day. 2 & 3 Vic., c. 74.

25th. *Bankers and Banking Companies* issuing notes payable on demand to lodge in Stamp Office, Dublin, an account of their places of business, partners, &c. 6 Geo. IV., c. 42.

25th. *Guardians of the Poor* to be elected for each Union, and those previously in office, not re-elected, to retire. [See February.] 1 & 2 Vic., c. 56.

26th. *Good Friday*, Holiday at Banks. Bills due this day payable on day previous. *Good Friday and Easter Eve* are Holidays in the Law Courts and Offices.

29th. *Easter Monday*, Holiday at the Banks and Public Offices. Bills due this day payable on day following. *Easter Monday and Tuesday* are Holidays at the Law Courts and Offices.

31st. *Interest on East India Bonds* due; payable on 1st April.

31st. *Dog Licences*—Last day for obtaining Licence (duty 2s for each dog) to keep a dog or dogs, from the Clerk of the Petty Sessions of the district where owner resides. 28 & 29 Vic., c. 50.

31st. *Refreshment House and Wine Licences* expire.

31st. *Hawkers' Licences* expire.

REGISTRY OF DOGS IN IRELAND.

By the Act for the Registration of Dogs every person is bound to take out a license on or before the 31st March in each year for each dog that he keeps. The license can be obtained by personal or written application to the Petty Sessions Clerk of each district, on payment of a fee of two shillings for each dog, and sixpence additional for the registry stamp. Full particulars of the sex, colour, breed, and description of the dog must be given. In case of the animal being transferred to another, it will not be necessary to renew the license until the expiration of the year for which it has been granted; but a certificate, with a sixpenny stamp attached, must be obtained from the Petty Sessions Clerk, and the certificate must be registered. This can be done without any extra fee. In the event of non-compliance with these regulations, the defaulter becomes liable to a penalty of 40s for neglecting to take out the license, and after the justice has imposed the fine the owner will be liable to a further penalty of 1s a-day for each day that he keeps an unlicensed dog. Every owner is bound to produce his license whenever required to do so, and in case of refusal is liable to a fine of 5s. Pups whelped after the 31st March need not be registered till the 31st March following.

April.

Days Month	Days Week	THE SUN		THE MOON			Souths		High Water at Derry Quay.			
		Rises	Sets	Rises Morn.	Sets Morn.	Age			Morn		Even	
		H M	H M	H M	H M		H	M	H	M	H	M
1	Thursday, ...	5 35	...	1 28	9 1	21	5	12	0	25	0	41
2	Friday, ...	...	6 37	2 15	10 15	22	6	12	1	25	1	49
3	Saturday, ...	5 29	...	2 51	11 34	23	7	8	2	21	2	45
4	SUNDAY, ...	...	6 41	3 17	aftern	24	8	0	3	12	3	36
5	Monday, ...	5 24	...	3 39	2 12	25	8	49	4	2	4	26
6	Tuesday, ...	...	6 44	3 56	3 28	26	9	35	4	38	5	12
7	Wednesday, ...	5 21	...	4 12	4 42	27	10	20	5	33	5	57
8	Thursday, ...	...	6 48	4 28	5 56	28	11	4	6	17	6	41
9	Friday, ...	5 15	...	4 44	7 7	N	11	48	7	1	7	25
10	Saturday, ...	...	6 51	5 3	8 19	1	0a	33	8	10	8	34
11	SUNDAY, ...	5 9	...	5 27	9 28	2	1	19	8	56	9	20
12	Monday, ...	...	6 56	5 55	10 33	3	2	7	9	44	10	8
13	Tuesday, ...	5 4	...	6 28	11 31	4	2	57	10	34	10	58
14	Wednesday, ...	...	6 59	7 11	morn	5	3	46	11	23	11	47
15	Thursday, ...	4 59	...	8 3	0 21	6	4	36	11	49	0	13
16	Friday, ...	...	7 3	9 4	1 2	7	5	25	0	38	1	2
17	Saturday, ...	4 55	...	10 10	1 34	8	6	12	1	25	1	49
18	SUNDAY, ...	...	7 7	11 20	2 0	9	6	59	2	12	2	36
19	Monday, ...	4 50	...	aftern	2 22	10	7	45	2	58	3	22
20	Tuesday, ...	...	7 11	1 48	2 41	11	8	31	3	44	4	8
21	Wednesday, ...	4 46	...	3 4	2 58	12	9	16	4	29	4	53
22	Thursday, ...	...	7 15	4 24	3 15	13	10	6	5	19	5	43
23	Friday, ...	4 41	...	5 49	3 34	14	10	58	6	11	6	35
24	Saturday, ...	...	7 19	7 15	3 55	F	11	54	7	7	7	31
25	SUNDAY, ...	4 37	...	8 43	4 23	16	morn		7	37	8	1
26	Monday, ...	...	7 22	10 5	4 58	17	0	54	8	30	8	54
27	Tuesday, ...	4 32	...	11 15	5 46	18	1	37	9	14	9	38
28	Wednesday, ...	...	7 26	morn	6 48	19	3	1	10	8	11	2
29	Thursday, ...	4 28	...	0 12	8 3	20	4	4	11	17	11	41
30	Friday, ...	...	7 30	0 52	9 23	21	5	3	0	16	0	40

PHASES OF THE MOON.

Last Quarter, Friday, 2nd day, at 13m. past 6, a.m.
New Moon, Friday, 9th day, at 7m. past 3, p.m.
First Quarter, Saturday, 17th day, at 14m. past 7, p.m.
Full Moon, Saturday, 24th day, at 50m. past 10, p.m.

BUSINESS REMEMBRANCER.

The Registers of Births, Deaths, and Marriages for the preceding three months must be copied and sent by the Registrars to the Superintendent Registrars, for transmission to the Registrar-General. 7 & 8 Vic., c. 81; 26 Vic., c. 11 & 27; and 26 & 27 Vic., c. 90.

Corporations, Companies, &c., in Receipt of Tolls to exhibit Accounts of Gross Receipts and Expenditure, to persons authorised to inspect them by Guardians of the Poor, during this month and October. 1 & 2 Vic., c. 56.

1st. *Booths and Tents* at Fairs or Races not to be open for sale of spirits, wine, or beer, except between the hours of *Nine* in the morning and *Six* in the evening, *from this date* to 1st October, nor to be open *before this date*, from 1st October, later than *Three* o'clock p.m., or earlier than *Nine*, a.m. 6 & 7 Wm. IV., c. 38.

1st. *Close season* for oysters in Tralee Bay, Achill Sound, and Blacksod Bay, 1st April to 1st October.

5th. *Game Certificates* (whole year and half-year) expire.

5th. *Dividends* for the half-year fall due on the following Government Securities:—3 per Cent. Reduced, and New 3 per Cent. Stock; payable on 6th. Dividend warrants will be transmitted by Post on application to the Banks of England or Ireland, one month and five days before. For the dividend due this day the application must be made not later than the 1st March.

9th. *Fire Insurance Premium* due 25th March must be paid on or before this day, or the Policy becomes void.

25th. *Dividends* due on Indian 4 per Cent. Transfer Loan Stock.

HOW TO TRAIN IVY.

As a permanent evergreen climber the ivy must be first, for it will grow anywhere, in sunshine or shade, in strong rich soil or in poor stony gravel; it will put up with almost any amount of ill-treatment, and positively thrives best when neglected. Of course, if it is required to put on an orderly appearance, such as when clothing the face of a dwelling-house, some attention must be given to it, particularly to the large-leaved varieties, as if allowed to grow unchecked to any great height on a vertical face, the loose, overhanging branches form a receptacle for snow in winter, the weight of which will sometimes tear down great breadths of it. In such positions ivy should never be nailed to the wall after the first season, if it can anyhow be avoided; it will be a saving of time in the end to wait until it clings naturally to the wall. To this end all loose branches should be cut off about the end of April or the first week in May, and it is at this time that walls that are already covered require annual attention; the whole face of the ivy should then be gone over with a pair of shears, cutting off all loose branches, and the greater portion of the leaves of the large-leaved kinds. As this is the time when the plant is on the point of breaking into its new growth, its denuded appearance will only last about a fortnight, when the whole face of the wall will be again covered by a surface of fresh, green leaves, and all branches formed near any uncovered portion of the wall will, from the vigour induced by the pruning, at once firmly cling to it. This annual pruning will cause the wall to be covered by a felt-like growth of branches, firmly attached, so that no violence of wind or weather will disturb it.— *From "Cassell's Household Guide."*

May.

Days Month	Days Week	THE SUN		THE MOON				High Water at Derry Quay.	
		Rises	Sets	Rises Morn.	Sets Morn.	Age	Souths	Morn	Even
		H M	H M	H M	H M		H M	H M	H M
1	Saturday, ...	4 24	...	1 21	10 43	22	5 57	1 10	1 34
2	SUNDAY, ...	...	7 33	1 44	aftern	23	6 47	2 0	2 24
3	Monday, ...	4 20	...	2 2	1 19	24	7 34	2 47	3 11
4	Tuesday, ...	...	7 37	2 19	2 32	25	8 18	3 31	3 55
5	Wednesday, ...	4 15	...	2 35	3 44	26	9 2	4 15	4 39
6	Thursday, ...	...	7 42	2 52	4 57	27	9 46	4 59	5 23
7	Friday, ...	4 11	...	3 9	6 7	28	10 30	5 43	6 7
8	Saturday, ...	...	7 45	3 30	7 16	29	11 16	6 29	6 53
9	SUNDAY, ...	4 7	...	3 56	8 23	N	0a 3	7 40	8 4
10	Monday, ...	...	7 49	4 28	9 23	1	0 52	8 29	8 53
11	Tuesday, ...	4 3	...	5 7	10 16	2	1 41	9 18	9 42
12	Wednesday, ...	...	7 53	5 57	10 59	3	2 31	10 8	10 32
13	Thursday, ...	4 0	...	6 56	11 34	4	3 20	10 57	11 21
14	Friday, ...	...	7 57	7 59	morn	5	4 7	11 18	11 42
15	Saturday, ...	3 56	...	9 8	0 1	6	4 54	0 8	0 32
16	SUNDAY, ...	3 58	8 0	10 19	0 25	7	5 38	0 51	1 15
17	Monday, ...	3 53	...	11 30	0 44	8	6 23	1 30	2 0
18	Tuesday, ...	...	8 2	aftern	1 1	9	7 8	2 21	2 45
19	Wednesday, ...	3 50	...	1 59	1 19	10	7 54	3 7	3 31
20	Thursday, ...	...	8 5	3 19	1 36	11	8 43	3 56	4 20
21	Friday, ...	3 47	...	4 41	1 56	12	9 36	4 49	5 13
22	Saturday, ...	...	8 9	6 9	2 19	13	10 34	5 47	6 11
23	SUNDAY, ...	3 44	...	7 35	2 50	14	11 36	6 49	7 13
24	Monday, ...	...	8 13	8 53	3 30	F	morn	7 37	8 1
25	Tuesday, ...	3 40	...	9 58	4 28	16	0 41	8 18	8 42
26	Wednesday, ...	...	8 15	10 47	5 38	17	1 47	9 24	9 48
27	Thursday, ...	3 37	...	11 20	7 0	18	2 50	10 27	10 51
28	Friday, ...	...	8 18	11 47	8 26	19	3 48	11 25	11 49
29	Saturday, ...	3 35	...	morn	9 47	20	4 41	11 54	0 18
30	SUNDAY, ...	...	8 21	0 8	11 7	21	5 31	0 44	1 8
31	Monday, ...	3 33	...	0 25	...	22	6 17	1 30	1 54

PHASES OF THE MOON.

Last Quarter, Saturday, 1st day, at 53m. past 1, p.m.
New Moon, Sunday, 9th day, at 16m. past 6, a.m.
First Quarter, Monday, 17th day, at 24m. past 10, a.m.
Full Moon, Monday, 24th day, at 39m. past 6, a.m.
Last Quarter, Sunday, 30th day, at 53m. past 10, p.m.

BUSINESS REMEMBRANCER.

1st. *Scotch Bank Holiday.*

1st. *Dredging for Oysters* prohibited generally between this date and 1st of September. 5 & 6 Vic., c. 106.

1st. *Maybush and Maypole* not to be put up, or suffered to remain by any person near his dwelling; penalty £2, or imprisonment. 15 & 16 Geo. III., c. 26.

1st. *Maybush or Maypole* not to be within 10 feet of any road in the County of Dublin; penalty £1—26 G. III., c. 14. Or on any part of a Post-road; penalty 10s—32 G. III., c. 30. Or on any road, or in any city, corporate or market town; penalty 10s—36 G. III., c. 55.

17th. *Whit Monday,* Holiday at the Banks. Bills due this day payable on the 18th. *Whit Monday and Tuesday,* Holidays in the Stamps and Taxes Offices, and in the Law Courts and Offices.

20th. *Savings Banks* to compute interest for a half-year to this date, and add amount to investments. 9 Geo. IV., c. 92.

24th. *Queen's Birth-day.* Holiday at Customs, Excise, and Stamps and Taxes Offices; and at Banks in Scotland.

29th. *Anniversary* of the restoration of Monarchy in Great Britain and Ireland. Holiday in the Stamps and Taxes Office.

PREVENTIVE FOR HYDROPHOBIA.—Dr. Rodet, chief surgeon of the Antiquaille, at Lyons, having remarked that a solution of perchloride of iron, applied as a tonic, was extremely useful in the treatment of certain disorders, was induced to try it also in cow-pox, and found, as he suspected, that the perchloride destroyed that virus completely. Encouraged by these results, he determined to try its effect on the virus of hydrophobia, and with this view a series of experiments were made at the Veterinary School of Lyons, from which it appears that the solution of perchloride of iron destroys the virus of hydrophobia with certainty, if applied within two hours of the infliction of the bite. It is highly probable that the effect would be the same if the remedy were applied four, six, or even eight hours later, but this requires confirmation by further experiment. Admitting that Dr. Rodet's discovery may be relied on, its importance cannot be overvalued; for although the actual cautery is exceedingly prompt, nay, instantaneous in its action, it is often difficult to apply it, either owing to the trepidation of the patent or to the dangerous position of the wound; and, on the other hand, it may often be easier to find the solution of perchloride at a chemist's, in the country especially, than a skilful operator to apply the red-hot iron unflinchingly to the injured part.

TREATMENT FOR DIPHTHERIA.—Within the past twelvemonth that dreadful disease, diphtheria, has considerably increased. In the early stages of the complaint, which is always accompanied by a soreness and swelling of the throat, let the patient use a simple solution of salt and water as a gargle, every fifteen minutes. At the same time moisten a piece of flannel with a solution of the same kind, made warm as the patient can bear it, and bind it around his throat, renewing it as often as the gargle is administered, and in the meanwhile sprinkling the fine salt between the flannel and the neck. Use inwardly some tonic or stimulant, either separately or, if the prostration be great, use both together. The treatment, as may be seen, is extremely simple, and, if used in the earlier stages of the disease, will effect a complete cure.

A MEMPHIS paper defines advertising to be a "blister which draws trade."

June.

Days Month	Days Week	THE SUN		THE MOON				High Water at Derry Quay.	
		Rises	Sets	Rises Morn.	Sets Aftern.	Age	Souths	Morn	Even
		H M	H M	H M	H M		H M	H M	H M
1	Tuesday, ...	3 33	...	0 41	1 35	23	7 1	2 14	2 38
2	Wednesday, ...	...	8 24	0 58	2 47	24	7 45	2 58	3 22
3	Thursday, ...	3 32	...	1 15	3 57	25	8 28	3 41	4 5
4	Friday, ...	...	8 25	1 36	5 7	26	9 13	4 26	4 50
5	Saturday, ...	3 30	...	1 59	6 13	27	10 0	5 13	5 37
6	SUNDAY, ...	...	8 27	2 28	7 16	28	10 48	6 1	6 25
7	Monday, ...	3 28	...	3 7	8 10	N	11 37	6 50	7 14
8	Tuesday, ...	...	8 29	3 54	8 57	1	0a 27	8 4	8 28
9	Wednesday, ...	3 28	...	4 48	9 35	2	1 16	8 53	9 17
10	Thursday, ...	...	8 31	5 56	10 5	3	2 4	9 41	10 5
11	Friday, ...	3 27	...	6 59	10 29	4	2 51	10 16	10 52
12	Saturday, ...	...	8 33	8 8	10 49	5	3 36	11 13	11 37
13	SUNDAY, ...	3 25	...	9 18	11 7	6	4 20	11 13	11 57
14	Monday, ...	...	8 34	10 30	11 25	7	5 4	0 17	0 41
15	Tuesday, ...	3 25	...	11 41	11 41	8	5 48	1 1	1 25
16	Wednesday, ...	...	8 35	aftern	11 58	9	6 34	1 47	2 11
17	Thursday, ...	3 25	...	2 18	morn	10	7 24	2 37	3 1
18	Friday, ...	...	8 35	3 40	0 18	11	8 17	3 30	3 54
19	Saturday, ...	3 25	...	5 6	0 45	12	9 16	4 29	4 53
20	SUNDAY, ...	...	8 36	6 27	1 19	13	10 19	5 26	5 50
21	Monday, ...	3 25	...	7 37	2 9	14	11 24	6 37	7 1
22	Tuesday, ...	...	8 36	8 35	3 12	F	morn	7 26	7 50
23	Wednesday, ...	3 26	...	9 17	4 31	16	0 30	8 7	8 31
24	Thursday, ...	...	8 36	9 48	5 57	17	1 32	9 9	9 33
25	Friday, ...	3 27	...	10 11	7 22	18	2 29	10 6	10 30
26	Saturday, ...	...	8 37	10 30	8 46	19	3 22	10 59	11 23
27	SUNDAY, ...	3 27	...	10 48	10 7	20	4 11	11 24	11 48
28	Monday, ...	...	8 38	11 5	11 21	21	4 57	0 10	0 34
29	Tuesday, ...	3 27	...	11 22	aftern	22	5 42	0 55	1 19
30	Wednesday, ...	...	8 39	11 40	1 47	23	6 26	1 39	2 3

PHASES OF THE MOON.

New Moon, Monday, 7th day, at 55m. past 9, p.m.
First Quarter, Tuesday, 15th day, at 52m. past 9, p.m.
Full Moon, Tuesday, 22nd day, at 46m. past 1, p.m.
Last Quarter, Tuesday, 29th day, at 57m. past 9, a.m.

BUSINESS REMEMBRANCER.

In this month *half-yearly* Return of Transfers, &c., to be made to the Registrar of Joint Stock Companies, by every Company *completely* registered under Act, and not afterwards incorporated. 7 & 8 Vic., c. 110.

1st. *Clerk of Peace in Counties* to make out and print Copy of Parliamentary Voters' Register for each Polling District separately. 13 & 14 Vic., c. 69, and Acts amending.

1st. *Clerk of Peace* to deliver Precept to Clerks of Unions, requiring revision of Register and Supplemental List of Ratepayers. *Ib.*

1st. *Clerk of Peace in Boroughs* to deliver his Precept to Town Clerk for publication of Notices, &c., under Parliamentary Voters' Act. *Ib.*

1st. *Clerk of Peace in Boroughs* to make out List of Parliamentary Voters for each Ward. *Ib.*

5th. *Town Clerks* to publish Notices requiring payment of Rates under Parliamentary Voters' Act. 13 & 14 Vic., c. 69.

13th. *Excise Licences*—Applications to renew licences, expiring 5th July, must be made on or before this day. 6 G. IV., c. 81.

14th. *Heath, Furze, &c.,* not to be burned on mountains, &c. (save where broken up for agriculture or planting), at any time before this day, from 2nd February. Penalty £5. 10 W. III., c. 8; 27 G. III., c. 35.

20th. *The forty-fourth year of Her Majesty's Reign* commences this day.

20th. *Male fallow Deer* may be killed between this date and 29th September following.

28th. *Poor-Rate Collectors* or Deputies to attend for receipt of Rates in respective Baronies, Boroughs, &c., on 1st July and three preceding days, exclusive of Sunday, at places to be named; due notice thereof being given. 13 & 14 Vic., c. 69.

30th. Within 14 days after this day and 31st December, Railway Companies to make an account of their Loan Capital raised. 29 & 30 Vic., c. 108.

THE MUMPS.—Several people have accused me in a friendly way of neglecting, in my Family Doctor articles, the ailments of children and old people. I plead guilty, but have a paper in preparation on some of the diseases incidental to childhood, and another on the ailments of the aged, which I trust will do good. I must here, however, take notice of one disease to which many of our little friends are subject—I mean the mumps. This is not a very dangerous disease, and can usually be treated at home, unless the inflammation shifts its quarters and attacks the breasts or the brain. The ailment consists of a swelling of the gland which we call the parotid, which lies in the cheek beneath the ear, but the inflammation generally extends also to the glands situated beneath the lower jaw. It is ushered in with some degree of fever, is at its worst about the fourth day, and rarely runs on to suppuration. The treatment is simplicity itself, consisting as it does of gentle laxatives, a non-stimulating or milk diet, confinement to the house, to prevent risk from exposure to cold and damp; a little fever mixture, such as a teaspoonful of the acetate of ammonia, with a few drops of sweet nitre in a little water four times a day, and the frequent application of warm fomentations, and the wearing round the neck of a poultice, or simply a roll or two of soft flannel.—*From " Cassell's Family Magazine"* *for April, 1879.*

THE man who does not advertise sells so little that he sells dear.

Days Month	Days Week	THE SUN		THE MOON				High Water at Derry Quay	
		Rises	Sets	Rises Morn.	Sets Aftern.	Age	Souths	Morn.	Even
		H M	H M	H M	H M		H M	H M	H M
1	Thursday, ...	3 28	...	...	2 58	24	7 11	2 24	2 48
2	Friday, ...	...	8 39	0 2	4 5	25	7 57	3 10	3 34
3	Saturday, ...	3 30	...	0 32	5 10	26	8 45	3 58	4 22
4	Sunday, ...	...	8 37	1 5	6 8	27	9 34	4 47	5 11
5	Monday, ...	3 33	...	1 49	6 57	28	10 23	5 36	6 0
6	Tuesday, ...	...	8 35	2 42	7 36	29	11 13	6 26	6 50
7	Wednesday, ...	3 35	...	3 43	8 9	N	0a 2	7 39	8 3
8	Thursday, ...	...	8 33	4 50	8 34	1	0 49	8 26	8 50
9	Friday, ...	3 37	...	5 59	8 56	2	1 35	9 12	9 36
10	Saturday, ...	...	8 32	7 8	9 14	3	2 19	9 56	10 20
11	Sunday, ...	3 39	...	8 20	9 31	4	3 3	10 40	11 4
12	Monday, ...	...	8 30	9 32	9 48	5	3 46	11 23	11 47
13	Tuesday, ...	3 41	...	10 44	10 5	6	4 31	11 44	0 8
14	Wednesday, ...	...	8 28	aftern	10 23	7	5 18	0 31	0 55
15	Thursday, ...	3 44	...	1 19	10 46	8	6 8	1 21	1 45
16	Friday, ...	...	8 26	2 40	11 16	9	7 3	2 16	2 40
17	Saturday, ...	3 46	...	4 2	11 56	10	8 2	3 15	3 39
18	Sunday, ...	...	8 23	5 15	morn	11	9 4	4 17	4 41
19	Monday, ...	3 49	...	6 19	0 51	12	10 8	5 21	5 45
20	Tuesday, ...	...	8 20	7 8	2 1	13	11 12	6 25	6 49
21	Wednesday, ...	3 52	...	7 45	3 23	F	morn	7 17	8 1
22	Thursday, ...	...	8 17	8 12	4 51	15	0 12	7 49	8 13
23	Friday, ...	3 55	...	8 32	6 16	16	1 8	8 45	9 9
24	Saturday, ...	...	8 14	8 52	7 39	17	1 59	9 36	9 60
25	Sunday, ...	3 58	...	9 8	9 0	18	2 48	10 25	10 49
26	Monday, ...	...	8 10	9 27	10 16	19	3 35	11 12	11 36
27	Tuesday, ...	4 3	...	9 45	11 31	20	4 21	11 34	11 58
28	Wednesday, ...	...	8 7	10 6	aftern	21	5 6	0 19	0 43
29	Thursday, ...	4 6	...	10 33	1 53	22	5 53	1 6	1 30
30	Friday, ...	...	8 4	11 5	3 0	23	6 40	1 53	2 17
31	Saturday, ...	4 9	...	11 46	4 0	24	7 29	2 42	3 6

PHASES OF THE MOON.

New Moon, Wednesday, 7th day, at 21m. past 1, p.m.
First Quarter, Thursday, 15th day, at 16m. past 6, a.m.
Full Moon, Wednesday, 21st day, at 2m. past 9, p.m.
Last Quarter, Wednesday, 28th day, at 41m. past 11, p.m.

BUSINESS REMEMBRANCER.

Registers of Births, Deaths, and Marriages for the preceding three months must be copied and sent during the month by the Registrars to the Superintendent Registrars for transmission to the Registrar-General. 7 & 8 Vic., c. 81 ; 26 Vic., c. 11 & 27 ; and 26 & 27 Vic., c. 90.

1st. *Dividends* on Bank of Ireland Stock payable.

1st. *Excise Licences* to Game Dealers expire.

1st. *Last day for payment of Poor Rates* due up to 1st January, to qualify for voting in Parliamentary Elections. 13 & 14 Vic., c. 69.

1st. *Poor-Rate Collectors, &c.,* may be required by Town Clerks to furnish Lists of Ratepayers in arrear. *Ib.*

1st. *Clerks of Peace* to send precepts to Clerks of Unions to prepare Baronial Lists of Jurors between 1st and 8th July. 34 & 35 Vic., c. 65.

5th. *Excise Licences* to appraisers, house agents, auctioneers, dealers in beer, spirits, wine, sweets, spirit dealers retailing spirits in bottle, tobacco dealers (except publicans), sweets retailers, chemists using stills, spirit grocers, tobacco manufacturers, vinegar makers, maltsters, malt-roasters, dealers in roasted malt, passage vessels, rectifiers and compounders, and plate dealers, expire.

Licences for the consumption of beer, ale, or porter elsewhere than on premises not to be granted in respect to premises rated at less than £8, or in towns with over 10,000 population, unless rated at £15 at least. 40 Vic., cap. 4.

8th. *Clerks of Unions* to make out Supplemental Lists of £12 Ratepayers for Clerk of Peace. 13 & 14 Vic., c. 69.

9th. *Clerks of Unions* to furnish Town Clerks with Lists of Ratepayers in Boroughs, &c. 13 & 14 Vic., c. 69.

9th. *Clerks of Unions* on or before this day to enter objections on Register of Voters received from Clerk of Peace. Last day for returning same to Clerk of Peace. *Ib.*

9th. *Fire Insurance Premium* due 24th June must be paid on or before this day, or Policy will become void.

19th. Last day for making out and issuing *Half-yearly Receipts for Interest* to Savings Banks and Friendly Societies. 7 & 8 Vic., c. 83.

20th. Last day for *Clerks of Peace* to enter objections to Parliamentary Voters on Register of Polling Districts; to be published on or before July 22. 13 & 14 Vic., c. 69.

20th. *Town Clerks* to make out Lists of Parliamentary Voters annually ; to be published on 22nd July. 13 & 14 Vic., c. 69, and Acts amending.

22nd. Last day for *Clerks of Peace* to publish notice requiring persons entitled to vote to send in their Claims. *Ib.*

22nd. *Clerks of Peace* to publish Register of Voters in each Polling District, with objections. *Ib.*

22nd. *Town Clerks* to publish Lists of Parliamentary Voters. *Ib.*

31st. Pawnbrokers' Licences expire.

HEALTHY TREATMENT FOR BOOTS AND SHOES.—For boots and shoes exposed to wet the following composition is recommended :—Linseed oil, one gill ; spirit of turpentine, one ounce ; beeswax, one ounce ; Burgundy pitch, half-an-ounce ; to be melted together and rubbed into the leather when quite dry, before the fire or in the hot sun. This composition will be found very effectual in preserving the leather both from rain and sea-water, and should come more generally into use in our uncertain climate.

Days Month	Days Week	THE SUN		THE MOON			Souths		High Water at Derry Quay	
		Rises	Sets	Rises Morn.	Sets Aftern.	Age			Morn	Even
		H M	H M	H M	H M		H M		H M	H M
1	Sunday, ...	4 11	...	...	4 53	25	8	18	3 31	3 55
2	Monday, ...	...	7 58	0 35	5 35	26	9	8	4 21	4 45
3	Tuesday, ...	4 14	...	1 34	6 10	27	9	57	5 10	5 34
4	Wednesday, ...	...	7 54	2 37	6 39	28	10	45	5 58	6 22
5	Thursday, ...	4 18	...	3 47	7 3	29	11	32	6 45	7 9
6	Friday, ...	...	7 50	4 57	7 21	N	0a	17	7 54	8 18
7	Saturday, ...	4 21	...	6 10	7 39	1	1	2	8 39	9 3
8	Sunday, ...	...	7 46	7 22	7 57	2	1	46	9 23	9 47
9	Monday, ...	4 24	...	8 34	8 12	3	2	30	10 7	10 31
10	Tuesday, ...	...	7 42	9 51	8 33	4	3	16	10 54	11 17
11	Wednesday, ...	4 28	...	11 8	8 52	5	4	5	11 18	11 42
12	Thursday, ...	...	7 37	aftern	9 19	6	4	57	0 7	0 31
13	Friday, ...	4 31	...	1 46	9 54	7	5	53	1 6	1 30
14	Saturday, ...	...	7 33	3 2	10 42	8	6	52	2 5	2 29
15	Sunday, ...	4 36	...	4 7	11 43	9	7	54	3 7	3 31
16	Monday, ...	...	7 29	5 0	morn	10	8	56	4 9	4 33
17	Tuesday, ...	4 40	...	5 40	0 57	11	9	56	5 9	5 33
18	Wednesday, ...	...	7 24	6 12	2 21	12	10	53	5 46	6 10
19	Thursday, ...	4 44	...	6 35	3 45	13	11	46	6 59	7 23
20	Friday, ...	...	7 19	6 55	5 10	F	morn		7 37	8 1
21	Saturday, ...	4 47	...	7 13	6 32	15	0	36	8 13	8 37
22	Sunday, ...	...	7 15	7 31	7 52	16	1	25	9 2	9 26
23	Monday, ...	4 51	...	7 51	9 8	17	2	12	9 49	10 13
24	Tuesday, ...	...	7 10	8 11	10 23	18	2	58	10 35	10 59
25	Wednesday, ...	4 55	...	8 35	11 35	19	3	45	11 22	11 46
26	Thursday, ...	...	7 6	9 5	aftern	20	4	33	11 45	0 9
27	Friday, ...	4 58	...	9 43	1 48	21	5	22	0 35	0 59
28	Saturday, ...	...	7 1	10 28	2 45	22	6	12	1 25	1 49
29	Sunday, ...	5 2	...	11 24	3 30	23	7	1	2 14	2 38
30	Monday, ...	...	6 56	morn	4 10	24	7	51	3 4	3 28
31	Tuesday, ...	5 5	...	0 26	4 40	25	8	30	3 52	4 16

PHASES OF THE MOON.

New Moon, Friday, 6th day, at 48m. past 3, a.m.
First Quarter, Friday, 13th day, at 42m. past 0, p.m.
Full Moon, Friday, 20th day, at 18m. past 5, a.m.
Last Quarter, Friday, 27th day, at 15m. past 4, p.m.

BUSINESS REMEMBRANCER.

Borough Taxes and Poor Rates, due on or before 31st May preceding, must be paid this month, to qualify Burgesses to vote at next Municipal Election. 3 & 4 Vic.; c. 108.

Notices relating to Votes for Members of Parliament belonging to any of the classes enumerated in the Acts 6 Vic., c. 18, and 13 & 14 Vic., c. 69, can be sent through the post (with the securities for their safe delivery enjoined by the Acts) on prepayment, in stamps, of the postage—whether inland or foreign, as the case may be—and of a registration fee of twopence, provided they be presented, duly directed, open and in duplicate, to the Postmaster of an office which is also a Money Order Office.

1st. *Overseers of Public Houses* to be appointed by two justices, at Petty Sessions or Police Office of the district, if not appointed by parishioners in Vestry. 6 & 7 Wm. IV., c. 38.

2nd. *Holiday* at the Banks. Bills due this day payable on the 3rd.

4th. Last day for sending to *Clerks of Peace* Claims to vote in Parliamentary Elections. 13 & 14 Vic., c. 69.

4th. Last day for sending to *Town Clerks* Claims to vote in Parliamentary Elections in Boroughs, &c. *Ib.*

9th. *Clerks of Peace* to make out Lists of persons who have made Claims to vote in Parliamentary Elections, to be published on or before 11th August. 13 & 14 Vic., c. 69.

11th. *Town Clerks* to publish List of persons claiming to vote in Boroughs, &c. 13 & 14 Vic., c. 69.

11th. *Clerks of Peace* to publish List of persons claiming to vote in Parliamentary Elections. *Ib.*

12th. *Grouse, Moor Game, or Heath Game* may be killed between this date and the 10th December following. Penalty, £5 a-head. 27 Geo. III., c. 35; 37 Geo. III., c. 21; 37 Vic., c. 11.

15th. *Clerks of Peace*, on or before this date, to make out baronial lists of Special Jurors. 34 & 35 Vic., c. 65.

20th. Last day for sending in *Notices of Objections* to persons registered or claiming to vote in Parliamentary Elections for Counties and Boroughs. 13 & 14 Vic., c. 69.

24th. *Clerks of Peace* to publish List of Parliamentary Voters Objected to in each Polling District, and *Town Clerks* to publish List of Voters in Boroughs, &c., Objected to. 24 & 25 Vic., c. 60.

25th. *Clerks of Peace*, after this date, to transmit to Chairman of Quarter Sessions an Abstract of Lists of Claimants and of persons Objected to. 13 & 14 Vic., c. 69, &c.

25th. *Town Clerks in Boroughs, &c.*, to deliver to Clerks of Peace copies of Lists of Parliamentary Voters, of Claimants, and of persons Objected to. *Ib.*

30th. *Railway Companies* to furnish Accounts to Board of Trade.

THE NIGHT AIR " CURE."—A certain Dr. Christian, who regards it as his distinctive medical mission to preach the unrecognised virtues of night air, says that it is important, when so many persons are trying all sorts of " cures"—water-cure, air-cure, milk-cure, whey-cure, and grape-cure—that the mind of convalescents should be roused to the perception of the exceptionally healing qualities of the night air. " Open your windows," he exclaims, " and allow the cool spirits of the night to enter your chamber, and to sweeten and calm your dreams."

No man ever lost money by judicious advertising.

September.

Days Month	Days Week	THE SUN		THE MOON			Souths		High Water at Derry Quay.	
		Rises	Sets	Rises Morn.	Sets Aftern.	Age			Morn	Even
		H M	H M	H M	H M		H M		H M	H M
1	Wednesday, ...	5 7	...	1 33	5 6	26	9 26		4 39	5 3
2	Thursday, ...	...	6 49	2 42	5 27	27	10 12		5 25	5 49
3	Friday, ...	5 11	...	3 53	5 45	28	10 57		6 10	6 34
4	Saturday, ...	...	6 44	5 6	6 5	N	11 42		6 54	7 18
5	SUNDAY, ...	5 14	...	6 19	6 21	1	0a 27		8 4	8 28
6	Monday, ...	...	6 39	7 36	6 39	2	1 14		8 51	9 15
7	Tuesday, ...	5 19	...	8 55	7 1	3	2 2		9 39	10 3
8	Wednesday, ...	...	6 33	10 13	7 25	4	2 54		10 31	10 55
9	Thursday, ...	5 22	...	11 33	7 57	5	3 49		11 26	11 50
10	Friday, ...	...	6 28	aftern	8 39	6	4 47		11 59	0 24
11	Saturday, ...	5 26	...	1 58	9 36	7	5 47		1 0	1 24
12	SUNDAY, ...	...	6 22	2 56	10 45	8	6 48		2 1	2 25
13	Monday, ...	5 31	...	3 38	morn	9	7 46		2 59	3 23
14	Tuesday, ...	...	6 17	4 12	0 3	10	8 43		3 56	4 20
15	Wednesday, ...	5 34	...	4 37	1 24	11	9 36		4 49	5 13
16	Thursday, ...	...	6 12	4 58	2 47	12	10 26		5 38	6 2
17	Friday, ...	5 38	...	5 17	4 7	13	11 15		6 25	6 49
18	Saturday, ...	...	6 7	5 35	5 28	F	11 37		6 50	7 14
19	SUNDAY, ...	5 42	...	5 54	6 44	15	0a 2		7 39	8 3
20	Monday, ...	...	6 2	6 15	8 0	16	0 49		8 26	8 50
21	Tuesday, ...	5 45	...	6 37	9 16	17	1 37		9 14	9 38
22	Wednesday, ...	...	5 57	7 6	10 27	18	2 25		10 2	10 26
23	Thursday, ...	5 49	...	7 41	11 33	19	3 14		10 51	11 15
24	Friday, ...	...	5 52	8 24	aftern	20	4 4		11 17	11 41
25	Saturday, ...	5 52	...	9 14	1 24	21	4 53		0 7	0 31
26	SUNDAY, ...	...	5 47	10 13	2 5	22	5 43		0 56	1 20
27	Monday, ...	5 56	...	11 18	2 39	23	6 31		1 44	2 8
28	Tuesday, ...	...	5 42	morn	3 7	24	7 19		2 32	2 56
29	Wednesday, ...	6 0	...	0 25	3 30	25	8 5		3 18	3 42
30	Thursday, ...	...	5 37	1 35	3 49	26	8 50		4 3	4 27

PHASES OF THE MOON.

New Moon, Saturday, 4th day, at 52m. past 4, p.m.
First Quarter, Saturday, 11th day, at 25m. past 6, p.m.
Full Moon, Saturday, 18th day, at 29m. past 3, p.m.
Last Quarter, Sunday, 26th day, at 9m. past 11, a.m.

BUSINESS REMEMBRANCER.

8th. *Town Clerk* of each Municipal Borough to prepare an alphabetical list of Burgesses; Collectors of local taxes attending to insert sums paid. 6 & 7 Vic., c. 93.

8th. *Revision Courts* under Parliamentary Voters Act to be held between 8th September and 25th October; notice thereof being given by Chairmen of Quarter Sessions and Clerks of Peace. 13 & 14 Vic. c. 69.

18th. *Publicans, Distillers, and Brewers* to give notice of application for renewal of licence, on or before this day. 6 G. IV., c. 81.

20th. *Partridge and Rail* may be killed between this date and the 10th January following. 27 Geo. III., c. 35; and 37 Geo. III., c. 21.

20th. *Partridge, Quail, Land Rail, or Wild Turkey* not to be taken, killed, exposed for sale, or purchased between 10th January and this date. Penalty, £5 a-head. *Ib.*

20th. *Town Clerks* to prepare Burgess Lists for each Ward, and allow access for perusal by all persons, without fee, until 30th, delivering a signed copy to Mayor on 20th. 6 & 7 Vic., c. 93.

22nd. *Town Clerks* to have a copy of Burgess Lists posted conspicuously from this day to 30th. 6 & 7 Vic., c. 93.

29th. *Reports* on the state of all *Establishments for Lunatic persons* to be made to the Lord Lieutenant of Ireland by Inspectors-General of Lunatic Asylums. 5 & 6 Vic., c. 123.

29th. *Chief Magistrates* to cause a Schedule of Corporation duties and tolls to be hung up in Market-houses every market day for a month after this date. 1 Geo. III., c. 17.

29th. *Ex-Officio Guardians* of the Poor to be selected for each Union from qualified Justices, not being Clergymen, Assistant-Barristers, or Stipendiaries. 1 & 2 Vic, c. 56.

30th. *Brewers' Excise Licences* expire.

30th. *Hawkers' Licences* for half-year expire.

SICK HEADACHE.—This complaint is the result of eating too much, and exerting too little. Nine times out of ten the cause is, in fact, that the stomach was not able to digest the food last introduced into it, either from its having been unsuitable or excessive in quantity. It is said a diet of bread and butter, with ripe fruits or berries, with moderate, continuous exercise in the open air, sufficient to keep up a gentle perspiration, would cure almost every case in a short time. Two teaspoonfuls of powdered charcoal, in half-a-glass of water, and drank, generally gives instant relief. We are inclined to think that the above remedies may do in some, but not in all cases. A sovereign remedy for this disease is not easily found. Sick headache is periodical, and is the signal of distress which the stomach puts up to inform us that there is an over-alkaline condition of its fluids; that it needs a natural acid to restore the battery to its normal working condition. When the first symptoms of a headache appear, take a teaspoonful of lime-juice clear fifteen minutes before each meal, and the same dose at bed-time; follow this up until all symptoms are passed, taking no other remedies, and you will soon be able to go free from your unwelcome nuisance. Many will object to this because the remedy is too simple, but many cures have been effected in this way.

IT is related of Dr. Garth, in his last illness, when he saw his fellow-doctors consulting together at his bedside, that he raised his head from the pillow and said, with a smile—"Dear gentlemen, let me die a natural death."

Days Month	Days Week	THE SUN		THE MOON					High Water at Derry Quay.	
		Rises	Sets	Rises Morn.	Sets Aftern.	Age	Souths		Morn	Even
		H M	H M	H M	H M		H	M	H M	H M
1	Friday, ...	6 3	...	2 48	4 8	27	9	35	4 48	5 12
2	Saturday, ...	...	5 33	4 1	4 25	28	10	20	5 33	5 57
3	SUNDAY, ...	6 7	...	5 17	4 44	29	11	6	6 19	6 43
4	Monday, ...	...	5 29	6 34	5 3	N	11	55	7 8	7 32
5	Tuesday, ...	6 11	...	7 56	5 28	1	0a	47	8 17	8 41
6	Wednesday, ...	...	5 23	9 16	5 59	2	1	42	9 19	9 43
7	Thursday, ...	6 15	...	0 38	6 41	3	2	41	10 18	10 42
8	Friday, ...	...	5 18	11 50	7 31	4	3	41	11 18	11 42
9	Saturday, ...	6 19	...	aftern	8 36	5	4	42	11 55	0 19
10	SUNDAY, ...	...	5 13	1 38	9 53	6	5	42	0 55	1 19
11	Monday, ...	6 23	...	2 13	11 12	7	6	38	1 51	2 15
12	Tuesday, ...	...	5 9	2 40	morn	8	7	31	2 44	3 8
13	Wednesday, ...	6 28	...	3 1	0 32	9	8	21	3 34	3 58
14	Thursday, ...	...	5 3	3 21	1 53	10	9	9	4 22	4 46
15	Friday, ...	6 32	...	3 39	3 10	11	9	56	5 9	5 33
16	Saturday, ...	...	5 0	3 58	4 27	12	10	42	5 55	6 19
17	SUNDAY, ...	6 35	...	4 17	5 41	13	11	29	6 42	7 6
18	Monday, ...	...	4 56	4 40	6 56	F	morn		7 37	8 1
19	Tuesday. ...	6 39	...	5 5	8 8	15	0	17	7 54	8 18
20	Wednesday, ...	...	4 52	5 38	9 15	16	1	5	8 42	9 6
21	Thursday, ...	6 43	...	6 18	10 19	17	1	55	9 32	9 56
22	Friday. ...	...	4 47	7 6	11 14	18	2	45	10 22	10 46
23	Saturday, ...	6 47	...	8 3	11 59	19	3	35	11 12	11 36
24	SUNDAY, ...	...	4 43	9 6	aftern	20	4	24	11 37	0 1
25	Monday, ...	6 51	...	10 10	1 6	21	5	11	0 26	0 50
26	Tuesday, ...	...	4 39	11 19	1 30	22	5	57	0 46	1 10
27	Wednesday, ...	6 55	...	morn	1 51	23	6	42	1 55	2 19
28	Thursday, ...	...	4 35	0 28	2 10	24	7	26	2 39	3 3
29	Friday. ...	6 59	...	1 38	2 28	25	8	10	3 23	3 47
30	Saturday, ...	...	4 30	2 53	2 47	26	8	56	4 9	4 33
31	SUNDAY, ...	7 3	...	4 8	3 5	27	9	43	4 56	5 20

PHASES OF THE MOON.

New Moon, Monday, 4th day, at 43m. past 4, a.m.
First Quarter, Monday, 11th day, at 35m. past 12, p.m.
Full Moon, Monday, 18th day, at 26m. past 4, a.m.
Last Quarter, Tuesday, 26th day, at 0m. past 7, a.m.

BUSINESS REMEMBRANCER.

Registers of Births, Deaths, and Marriages for the preceding three months must be sent by the Registrars to the Superintendent Registrars, for transmission to the Registrar-General. 7 & 8 Vic., c. 81; 26 Vic., c. 11 & 27; and 26 & 27 Vic., c. 90.

Notice of intended Application for any Railway Act to be inserted in *Dublin Gazette* and local Newspapers in October or November.

Corporations, Companies, &c., in Receipt of Tolls to exhibit Accounts of Gross Receipts and Expenditure to persons authorised to inspect them by Guardians of the Poor, during this month and April. 1 & 2 Vic., c. 56.

1st. *Pheasants* may be killed between this date and 31st January following. 28 & 29 Vic., c. 54.

1st. *Notices of Objections* to Burgesses inserted in Lists, *and of Claims* to be inserted, must *on this day* be given to Town Clerks, and the former left at premises of persons objected to. 6 & 7 Vic., c. 93.

1st. Methylated Spirit Makers' and Sellers' *Excise Licences* expire.

1st. *Boards of Conservators of Fisheries* to be elected for the three years ensuing. 25 & 26 Vic., c. 114.

7th. *Latest Day for Notice* to be given by Clerks of Town Commissioners for annual Election under Towns Improvement Act, to supply the place of Commissioners going out by rotation on 15th of this month. 17 & 18 Vic., c. 103.

10th. *Publicans and Distillers' Licences* expire this day. Notice for application for renewal to be given *twenty-one* days previously. 6 Geo. IV., c. 81.

12th. *Municipal Borough Lists of Objections and Claims* to be posted conspicuously in Borough for 8 days next preceding 20th October. *Town Clerks* to keep copies of Lists for perusal during same time, without fee. 6 & 7 Vic., c. 93.

14th. *Fire Insurance* Premium due at Michaelmas must be paid on or before this day, or the Policy becomes void.

15th, or next lawful day, *one-third of Commissioners under Towns Improvement Act* to go out of office, and an equal number to be elected. Hours for polling, 9 to 4. 17 & 18 Vic., c. 103.

17th. *Return of Commissioners* elected under Towns Improvement Act to be published by Returning Officer not later than this day, at 2 o'clock; and notice to be given by him to persons elected. *Ib.*

19th. Last day for delivering over voting papers and poll books used in the election of Town Commissioners to Clerk of the Commissioners, for custody and for inspection on payment of fee of 1s. *Ib.*

20th. *Revision of Burgess Lists* to be made between this day and 10th November. 6 & 7 Vic., c. 93.

25th. *Revision Courts* under Parliamentary Voters Act to be held between 8th September and 25th October; notice thereof being given by Chairmen of Quarter Sessions and Clerks of Peace. 13 & 14 Vic., c. 69.

31st. *Game Certificates* (half-year) expire.

LET us look upon each day as a sheet of white paper which has been placed in our hands to be covered with characters which will never be effaced, and take care to write nothing on this sheet which we would object to have read a thousand years hence.

November.

Days Month	Days Week	THE SUN		THE MOON				High Water at Derry Quay.	
		Rises	Sets	Rises Morn.	Sets Aftern.	Age	Souths	Morn	Even
		H M	H M	H M	H M		H M	H M	H M
1	Monday, ...	7 6	...	5 30	3 27	28	10 34	5 47	6 11
2	Tuesday, ...	...	4 21	6 53	3 57	N	11 28	6 33	7 3
3	Wednesday, ...	7 9	...	8 14	4 34	1	0a 27	8 4	8 28
4	Thursday, ...	...	4 16	9 33	5 21	2	1 29	9 6	9 30
5	Friday, ...	7 13	...	10 41	6 24	3	2 32	10 9	10 33
6	Saturday, ...	...	4 12	11 33	7 40	4	3 34	11 11	11 35
7	SUNDAY, ...	7 18	...	aftern	9 2	5	4 33	11 46	0 10
8	Monday, ...	...	4 8	0 44	10 23	6	5 24	0 41	1 5
9	Tuesday, ...	7 22	...	1 8	11 43	7	6 19	1 32	1 56
10	Wednesday, ...	...	4 3	1 27	morn	8	7 7	2 20	2 44
11	Thursday, ...	7 25	...	1 45	1 0	9	7 53	3 6	3 30
12	Friday, ...	...	4 0	2 3	2 16	10	8 39	3 52	4 16
13	Saturday, ...	7 30	...	2 22	3 29	11	9 25	4 38	5 2
14	SUNDAY, ...	...	3 57	2 43	4 42	12	10 11	5 24	5 48
15	Monday, ...	7 34	...	3 8	5 53	13	10 59	6 12	6 36
16	Tuesday ...	...	3 54	3 39	7 3	F	11 48	7 1	7 25
17	Wednesday, ...	7 38	...	4 15	8 10	15	morn	7 37	8 1
18	Thursday, ...	...	3 50	5 0	9 7	16	0 39	8 16	8 40
19	Friday, ...	7 43	...	5 54	9 56	17	1 29	9 6	9 30
20	Saturday, ...	...	3 47	6 55	10 35	18	2 18	9 55	10 19
21	SUNDAY, ...	7 46	...	7 58	11 7	19	3 6	10 43	11 7
22	Monday, ...	...	3 44	9 5	11 33	20	3 52	11 29	11 53
23	Tuesday, ...	7 50	...	10 13	11 54	21	4 37	11 50	0 14
24	Wednesday, ...	...	3 42	11 22	aftern	22	5 20	0 33	0 57
25	Thursday, ...	7 53	...	morn	0 31	23	6 3	1 16	1 40
26	Friday, ...	...	3 40	0 31	0 48	24	6 46	1 59	2 23
27	Saturday, ...	7 56	...	1 45	1 8	25	7 32	2 45	3 9
28	SUNDAY, ...	...	3 38	2 59	1 27	26	8 19	3 32	3 56
29	Monday, ...	8 0	...	4 21	1 52	27	9 11	4 24	4 48
30	Tuesday, ...	...	3 37	5 43	2 25	28	10 7	5 22	5 46

PHASES OF THE MOON.

New Moon, Tuesday, 2nd day, at 55m. past 3, p m.
First Quarter, Tuesday, 9th day, at 20m. past 8, a.m.
Full Moon, Tuesday, 16th day, at 39m. past 8, p.m.
Last Quarter, Thursday, 25th day, at 5m. past 2, a.m.

BUSINESS REMEMBRANCER.

Notice of intended Application for any Railway Act to be inserted in *Dublin Gazette* and local Newspapers in October or November.

1st. *Close Season* for fishing for salmon with single rod and line from this day to 1st February.

10th. *Revision of Burgess Lists* to be made between 20th October and this date. 6 & 7 Vic., c. 93.

15th. *Collectors of Poor Rates* to deliver to Clerk of Union a List of Tenements requiring revision. Penalty for neglect, £5. 17 Vic., c. 8, s. 4.

15th. *Clerks of Peace* (except for the *City of Dublin* and *County of Cork*) shall post notices of times and places fixed for holding Quarter Sessions for next year, on or before this day, and also six weeks before each Session; the *Easter Sessions* shall be held on any of the fourteen days next after the 25th of March; the *Summer Sessions*, on any day between the 4th and 12th day next after the last day of Trinity Term, both days inclusive; the *October Sessions*, on any of the fourteen days next after the 8th October; and the *Hilary Sessions*, on any of the fourteen days

next after 26th December. 14 & 15 Vic., c. 57.

20th. *Town Clerks* to have Burgess Roll completed this day from revised lists. 5 & 6 Vic., c. 93.

20th. *Savings Banks Investments* to have a half-year's interest added. The surplus fund of the year to be transferred to Commissioners for Reduction of National Debt. Accounts of progress, &c., for the year to be made up to this day, and transmitted to Commissioners within nine weeks. 9 Geo. IV., c. 92; and 7 & 8 Vic., c. 83.

25th. *Borough Councillors* to be elected. 5 & 6 Vic., c. 93.

27th. *Clerks of Union* to make out a complete List of all Tenements referred to in Rate Collectors' Lists, and transmit same to the Commissioner of Valuation. 17 Vic., c. 8.

30th. *Plans, Sections, and Books of Reference, relating to any projected line of Railway*, must be deposited on or before this day, with the Clerk of the Peace, and at the Board of Trade, London, prior to application to Parliament for Act of Incorporation.

POTATO PLANTING.—Generally speaking, the best time to plant potatoes is late in October or early in November. The reason for this is not far to seek. Potatoes, if stored in a cellar until spring, shoot forth long roots or filaments, called by different names in different counties, and thus expend their vegetative power before they are planted, and are thus far more liable to disease. They are, in fact, sickly potatoes; and matters are not much mended by storing seed potatoes in a garret, for there they shrivel, and thus lose much of their strength of growth; whereas, if planted in the autumn, they are kept alike from the outward air and from growth, and thus come out of the ground in the spring stronger and better plants than those put in in the early spring. The potatoes should be planted a couple of inches deeper than usual.

THE HAWTHORN should be cultivated as a winter or early spring plant for the conservatory. The white variety seems more willing to flower than the red or pink kinds, but all are worthy of attention. On the 1st September we lifted six plants from a thicket, planted two or three years ago, potted them in 10-in. pots, using a stiff clayey loam, with a good mixture of sand, and placed them behind a north wall, where they remained with no further attention until the 5th of November, when they were introduced into a vinery, and were soon a perfect sheet of blossom.—*Gardening Illustrated.*

December.

Days Month	Days Week	THE SUN		THE MOON				High Water at Derry Quay.	
		Rises	Sets	Rises Morn.	Sets Aftern.	Age	Souths	Morn	Even
		H M	H M	H M	H M		H M	H M	H M
1	Wednesday, ...	8 3	....	7 6	3 9	29	11 8	6 21	6 45
2	Thursday, ...	...	3 34	8 20	4 5	N	0a 11	7 48	8 12
3	Friday, ...	8 6	...	9 22	5 19	1	1 17	8 54	9 18
4	Saturday, ...	...	3 33	10 8	6 41	2	2 20	9 57	10 21
5	SUNDAY, ...	8 9	...	10 43	8 4	3	3 19	10 56	11 20
6	Monday, ...	...	3 32	11 11	9 28	4	4 13	11 26	11 50
7	Tuesday, ...	8 12	...	11 32	10 48	5	5 4	0 17	0 41
8	Wednesday, ...	...	3 31	11 53	morn	6	5 51	1 4	1 28
9	Thursday, ...	8 15	...	aftern	0 6	7	6 38	1 51	2 15
10	Friday, ...	...	3 30	0 29	1 20	8	7 23	2 36	3 0
11	Saturday, ...	8 18	...	0 49	2 33	9	8 9	3 22	3 46
12	SUNDAY, ...	...	3 30	1 11	3 44	10	8 56	4 9	4 33
13	Monday, ...	8 20	...	1 39	4 54	11	9 44	4 57	5 21
14	Tuesday, ...	...	3 30	2 13	5 59	12	10 34	5 47	6 11
15	Wednesday, ...	8 22	...	2 56	6 1	13	11 24	6 36	7 0
16	Thursday, ...	...	3 30	3 46	7 52	F	11 49	7 2	7 26
17	Friday, ...	8 24	...	4 45	8 35	15	0 13	7 50	8 14
18	Saturday, ...	...	3 30	5 48	9 9	16	1 2	8 39	9 3
19	SUNDAY. ...	8 25	...	6 55	9 37	17	1 49	9 26	9 50
20	Monday, ...	...	3 31	8 3	9 59	18	2 34	10 11	10 35
21	Tuesday, ...	8 26	...	9 0	10 20	19	3 17	10 54	11 18
22	Wednesday, ...	...	3 31	10 17	10 36	20	4 0	11 13	11 37
23	Thursday, ...	8 27	...	11 27	10 53	21	4 22	11 37	0 1
24	Friday, ...	...	3 32	morn	11 11	22	5 25	0 38	1 2
25	Saturday, ...	8 27	...	0 39	11 20	23	6 10	1 23	1 47
26	SUNDAY, ...	...	3 34	1 56	11 50	24	6 58	2 11	2 35
27	Monday, ...	8 28	...	3 14	aftern	25	7 50	3 3	3 27
28	Tuesday, ...	...	3 36	4 33	0 55	26	8 47	4 0	4 24
29	Wednesday, ...	8 28	...	5 52	1 43	27	9 49	5 2	5 26
30	Thursday, ...	...	3 38	7 0	2 47	28	10 53	6 6	6 30
31	Friday, ...	8 27	...	7 55	4 6	N	11 58	7 11	7 35

PHASES OF THE MOON.

New Moon, Thursday, 2nd day, at 56m. past 2, a.m.
First Quarter, Wednesday, 8th day, at 38m. past 6, p.m.
Full Moon, Thursday, 16th day, at 36m. past 3, p.m.
Last Quarter, Friday, 24th day, at 57m. past 6, p.m.
New Moon, Friday, 31st day, at 56m. past 1, p.m.

BUSINESS REMEMBRANCER.

1st. *Borough Council* to elect a Mayor out of the Aldermen or Councillors—to enter office on the 1st January. 6 & 7 Vic., c. 93.

3rd. *Borough Auditors and Assessors* (two of each) to be elected by the whole body of qualified Burgesses; and two Assessors for each Ward, to be elected by its Burgesses. 5 & 6 Vic., c. 93.

10th. *Grouse, Moor Game, or Heath Game* not to be taken, killed, sold, or exposed for sale, or purchased, between this date and 12th August following. Penalty, £5 a-head. 27 Geo. III., c. 35; 37 Geo. III., c. 21; and 37 Vic., c. 11.

12th. *Parliamentary Notices* under the Standing Orders of either House of Parliament, required to be served on or before the 15th December, must be posted not later than the 12th December, unless the 12th fall on a Sunday, when they must be posted not later than the 11th; but those notices which, by the same orders, may be served after the 15th, may be posted after the 12th of that month, provided they are posted at the General Post Office, Dublin, or one or other of the following Post Offices in Ireland:—Athlone, Belfast, and Cork. The words "Parliamentary Notice" must be legibly printed on the face of the letter; the postage must be prepaid in stamps, and a registration fee of 6d (in money) at the time of posting, which may be known by applying to the above offices. Duplicate lists of the addresses must be sent with the notices, which must be arranged in same order as entered on the lists.

23rd. On or before this day application to be made to all *Owners, Lessees,* and *Occupiers of Land* affected by any proposed Railway; and plans, sections, and books of reference to be deposited with Clerks of Poor-Law Unions, and at Private Bill Office, House of Commons.

25th. *Christmas Day* and the seven days following are Holidays in the Law Courts and Offices.

25th. *County Treasurers* to transmit to Chief Secretary for Ireland, before this day, copies of all Presentments made and fiated; to be laid before Parliament. Forfeiture of office for neglect. 6 & 7 W. IV., c. 116.

26th. *Holiday* at the Banks. Bills due this day payable on 24th.

31st. *Pedlars' Certificates* expire this day. Application for renewal to be made at Police Station of the district within which applicant resides. 34 & 35 Vic., c. 96.

31st. *Commissioners of Drainage* to lay annual accounts before Parliament on the first meeting after this date. 5 & 6 Vic., c. 89.

31st. *Clerks of Peace* to sign and deliver to Returning Officer the Book containing the revised List of Voters in Boroughs, &c., on or before this day. 13 & 14 Vic., c. 69.

31st. *Clerks of Peace* to sign and deliver to Sheriff the General and Special Jurors' Books for this year on or before this day. 34 & 35 Vic., c. 65, sec. 13.

GAINING INFORMATION.—Locke was asked how he had contrived to accumulate a mine of knowledge so rich, yet so extensive and deep. He replied that he attributed what little he knew to the not having been ashamed to ask for information, and to the rule he had laid down of conversing with all descriptions of men on those topics chiefly that formed their own particular professions and pursuits. The best informed men are undoubtedly those who adopt this rule.

GARDENING OPERATIONS.

JANUARY.

In many respects this month affords but few opportunities for garden operations. However, this must not be an excuse for inactivity, as there are a variety of matters deserving of careful attention.

FRUITS.—In mild, open weather the transplanting of fruit trees may be proceeded with, care being taken not to plant in too deep, or in an extra rich soil, as it will be found that apples, pears, and plums are more prolific when planted in soil of medium quality. In all cases the ground must be well prepared, and where the soil is deep or retentive a stratum of ashes, or such like substance, will be found useful in preventing the downward tendency of the roots. Loam from old pasture forms the best description of soil for the healthy and productive development of fruit trees. Scions of choice fruit trees for grafting should be secured, having regard only to such varieties as experience has proved to be well adapted to the locality. The selection must be taken only from trees which are perfectly free from disease, and, after removing the embryo buds from the parts to be placed in the ground, they ought to be deposited in a moist soil behind a north wall. In fine weather prune and train wall fruit trees; finish pruning currants, gooseberries, and raspberries, and add a good dressing of well-rotted manure round the bushes.

FLOWERS.—Pits, frames, soils, and pots should be got into immediate readiness. As soon as the weather permits, any alterations in the grounds that have been decided on should be carried out with as little delay as possible. Remove all fallen leaves, and slightly rake the borders to make up by neatness what is wanting in attractiveness; provide turf sods or willow dust for auriculas, cow manure for ranunculuses, and stable manure for carnations and picotés, all of the best descriptions, and, if possible, keep under cover; examine dahlia roots, and store away in a moderately dry place; avoid damp for auriculas and polyanthus, and admit to both abundance of fresh air; protect from frost hyacinths, tulips, anemones, and ranunculuses planted in autumn, also tender evergreens and flowering shrubs; transplant roses, and mulch them with a few inches of short dung; plant anemones and ranunculuses; sow sweet peas for early flowering; dig vacant flower plots for vegetables.

VEGETABLES.—Let trenching of vacant ground be proceeded with immediately, except in wet or severe frosty weather; attend to the forcing of rhubarb, seakale, and asparagus; examine cauliflower and lettuce frames, divest of decaying foliage, and protect from slugs by carefully sprinkling a little lime or soot over the surface of the soil; sow early peas and beans in sheltered situations, and protect from frost those sown in autumn by inserting spruce twigs along each side of the rows; plant early York and nonpariel cabbages, and ashleaf kidney or other early potatoes in warm borders.

FEBRUARY.

FRUITS.—Whatever pruning has been neglected should be attended to at once. The training and planting of young trees may be carried on with advantage in mild, dry weather; top-dress fruit-tree borders with short manure; fork over the ground about fruit bushes, and apply manure water to gooseberries and currants; protect peaches on the open wall which show any appearance of fruit; attend to recently-planted trees, and encourage with short manure about the roots; remove large trees which may be condemned, and all decaying branches from those that are to remain.

FLOWERS.—This is the month to top-dress roses. Protect from frost all autumn-planted bulbs and early-flowering plants; pansies, pinks, and carnations in open ground require attention; guard crocuses from vermin, and plant anemones and ranunculuses, which will thrive in any common garden soil. Gladioli may be planted in pots, and kept in a cold frame till the severe frosts are over, when they should be planted in their permanent quarters; plant daisies, auriculas, primroses, and other spring-flowering plants; propagate herbaceous plants by dividing the roots; trim box edgings, and fill up vacant spots; sow hardy annuals in pans to succeed those sown in autumn.

VEGETABLES.—Two sowings of peas, if weather permits, should be made. Broad beans may also be sown twice, care being taken of the earlier crops; the main crop should be got in by the end of the month. Sow early carrots, lettuces, and radishes, in warm and well-protected beds; prepare ground for onions by trenching and heavy manuring—top-dress with soot and a sprinkling of salt; plant a small quantity of the earliest sorts of potatoes, in the warmest positions, at least six inches deep; artichokes, rhubarb, and seakale may be got in; towards the end of the month a small sowing of parsnips may be made in deep soil; stir the surface of the soil among young cauliflowers, and remove all decayed or decaying leaves; dust a little soot among strawberry plants for the purpose of destroying snails—fork over and manure the spaces between the rows, being careful not to disturb the roots; transplant Tripoli onions; sow in hot-beds cauliflower and salads; earth up savoys, borecole, and other winter crops; manure and dig ground for early cropping.

MARCH.

FRUITS.—Grafting of fruit trees must now be proceeded with. The blossoms of plums, cherries, and peach trees should get a slight dusting of soot on a dewy morning, to protect them from birds, and a little labour will not be lost in painting apple and pear trees with a mixture of lime, sulphur, and tobacco liquid, with as much soot as will take away the glaring colour of the lime, which will prevent the growth of mosses and destroy any insects that may infest the branches; gooseberries, currants, and raspberries should be staked and tied; the pruning of climbers should be completed as soon as possible; trees coming into bloom must be well guarded against frost by a covering of matting.

FLOWERS.—As appearances are everything, care should be taken to make up for bleakness by re-gravelling the walks and keeping the edgings tidy. In fine weather sow sweet peas, mignionette, candytufts, Virginian stocks, and such-like hardy annuals; asters and other tender plants may be sown in pots or hot-beds; protect all autumn-planted bulbs from frost, and transplant autumn-sown annuals to places where they are intended to flower; finish digging and manuring vacant flower-ground; prune roses; sow lawn grass seeds for making a new lawn, or on bare patches on the lawn already formed to renovate it; roll lawns, and keep the grass short.

VEGETABLES.—A few small beds or rows of early horn carrots should be sown in this month, and the general crop in beginning of next. Should the weather prove favourable the main crops of potatoes, parsnips, peas, beans, cabbage, &c., should be sown; towards the end of the month sow, in a warm, sheltered place, Brussels sprouts and brocoli; sow once a fortnight marrowfoot peas, long-pod and Windsor beans, spinage, orange jelly and white Dutch turnips, lettuces, radishes, mustard, and cress, and in hot-beds celery, cauliflowers, and small salads; plant autumn-sown cabbages, early and late varieties, for principal crops; protect and rod all early peas as they advance; plant out cauliflowers, taking care to protect by spruce branches in severe weather.

APRIL.

FRUITS.—Wall trees will now require the utmost attention, and must be strictly guarded from frost, only exposing the trees in warm weather; remove all superfluous buds; finish the pruning of roses, and use every precaution to prevent the ravages of insects and birds on the early bloom; transplant holly in mild, showery weather; any shrubs that require pruning or dressing should be attended to at once; graft apple and pear trees; the ground about gooseberry and currant bushes should be frequently turned over, and stems and young leaves well watched for the appearance of caterpillars, slugs, and other pests, which destroy as soon as they appear; clear away suckers from trees and bushes, digging towards the roots for that purpose, if necessary.

FLOWERS.—Remove primroses and other varieties of the polyanthus tribe as soon as they cease blooming, to give room for summer flowering plants; complete the sowing of hardy annuals and biennials; sow for mignonette, stocks, and asters; plant out wall-flowers, sweet-williams, &c.; look carefully over your roses after curled leaves, which will be found to contain a grub that will prove destructive to the bloom if unmolested; pot off, or plant in frames or boxes, young cuttings, as soon as they are sufficiently rooted; strike cuttings of good varieties of dahlias, and keep growing those which have already been potted; as potted plants become established, they must be gradually inured to the open air; roll grass lawns frequently, keeping them well mown, and the edges of walks and beds trim and clean.

VEGETABLES.—Sow peas in the first and last week. At the beginning of the month sow in glass shades kidney beans and scarlet runners; plant out cabbages, lettuces, and cauliflowers; finish planting of seakale, rhubarb, and asparagus; get in the main crop of potatoes, cabbage, carrots, parsnips, leeks, onions, parsley, &c., if not completed last month; from the middle to the end of the month sow for the first crop beet-root, thyme, lavender, and all kinds of herbs; sow in hotbeds tomatoes, celery, and vegetable marrow; fork or stir up the soil between the rows of crops as they advance; continue the sowing of lettuce, and water the young plants constantly in dry weather; plant slips of herbs in shady places; earth up the rows of peas, beans, and all kinds of the cabbage tribe; be unremitting in keeping down weeds. For seed-sowing choose a dry day and dry soil, if possible.

MAY.

FRUITS.—Take away all superfluous buds in peaches and apricots on walls, allowing only to remain as many shoots as can be used without crowding, and where the young shoots promise to be too strong they should be stopped after they have made a few leaves. This will moderate the growth in other parts of the tree, and will help to spread the sap more regularly over the whole plant. If the fruit should appear rather abundant it will be necessary to thin out in such places as may be most needed, which can be best accomplished when the fruit has grown to the size of a bean. To keep the fruit clean and free from insects they should be occasionally syringed with soapsuds, or such other preparation as may be considered desirable. Suckers should be instantly removed, and the growth of young wood on vines should be checked, as, if neglected, the strength of the main stems will be injured, and the fruit will not come to maturity. The soil between the rows of strawberries should be gently stirred up, and all unnecessary runners cut off. Trees recently planted require to be watered in dry weather, and those in bloom must be well guarded against frost.

FLOWERS.—This is undoubtedly the busiest month in the year in the flower garden, as it will be the desire to have everything in neat order, which is sometimes difficult to accomplish owing to the amount of attention necessary to be given to the preparation of beds for the young plants, and the process of bedding out. The flower-beds, which have been awaiting their summer occupants, must be nicely dug over, and in many cases re-formed, so as to prevent any delay at the end of the month, which will be found best suited for removing the young plants to that position which they are intended to beautify; the edges must be neatly squared, and everything got into perfect trim. Calceolaries may be planted as soon as favourable weather permits. Bedding plants which have hitherto been confined to pits or frames must be gradually exposed during the day, and sufficient air admitted at night, as may, when removed, act as a safeguard against any check to their growth when finally planted out; when planted out the greatest care is necessary, especially in dry weather, to water liberally, and protect from extreme cold or heat. Sow hardy annuals for succession, and thin out last month's sowings, if coming up too thick; propagate heartsease and wallflowers by cuttings, and plant out dahlias in holes eighteen inches deep. Look carefully after creepers, training the young shoots as soon as they get long enough, and cutting off badly-placed or untidy growths. Make layers of fuchsias in the same manner as carnations so soon as the stems are well grown, and they will be fine plants in the autumn. Keep rose-buds and young leaves free of green fly and caterpillar. Attend well to grass lawns, walks, &c.

VEGETABLES.—In this department great watchfulness is required, as there will be an accumulation of pests, in the shape of weeds, insects, and caterpillars, the latter of which are most avaricious and very destructive to young plants, especially cabbages and cauliflowers; to protect from the ravages of slugs and other insects, strew soot or lime round about the plants. Continue the sowing of beans, cabbage, lettuce, radish, spinage, turnips, brocoli, mustard, and cress; towards end of month make the first sowing of endive; plant leeks and onions on well-manured soil, also cabbages, lettuces, and cauliflowers for the principal crop; plant tomatoes against a wall with a southern aspect; thin out parsnips and weed seed beds; dig and manure ground as it becomes vacant; rod peas and earth them up; prick out cauliflower, brocoli, and celery plants into beds; keep the soil loose in potatoe beds, and earth up where necessary; guard gooseberries from the ravages of the caterpillar. In cases where this cannot be performed with the hand, a good sprinkling of lime water has been found fairly effective.

JUNE.

FRUITS.—Gooseberries and currants on walls must have their leading shoots tied in to prevent their being broken; thin out the young shoots from raspberries, leaving six or eight of the best, which will produce strong canes to form arches at the ensuing winter pruning; thin apricots; train and prune all summer shoots of wall and trellis trees; pay careful attention to strawberries, keeping them and all spring-transplanted trees and bushes well watered in dry weather; pinch young shoots of all wall fruit trees not required for the formation of the tree; nail and train those that are required; pinch or thin out shoots of currants, gooseberries, &c.; clear away young suckers or other superfluous shoots that may be growing from the roots of trees; protect cherry trees from the ravages of black-fly, by dipping the points infested by it in a mixture of clayey soil and water, which will quickly dry in the sun, and may be washed off when the insects have perished; look over vines, and cut away weak and useless growths.

FLOWERS.—Pay careful attention to roses, the budding of which may be performed towards the end of the month, selecting buds from the strongest shoots; thin, transplant, and stake dahlia shoots; plant out pansy seedlings and cuttings in shady places for late bloom; harvest and carefully lay past tulips, crocuses, and all autumn-planted bulbs, as soon as the foliage dies down, drying them gradually in a shady place; propagate verbenas, heliotropes, &c., by cuttings; tie up carnations; keep bedded-out plants well watered in sultry weather, which should be done after sunset. As the young plants advance some will require to be tied up, while, on the other hand, some will require pegging down. In the latter case the plants should be given a northern aspect, as the young laterals will be drawn by the light of the sun toward other points, and the beds will acquire a well-filled appearance.

VEGETABLES.—This is the proper season for planting out such vegetables as cauliflowers, kale, Brussels sprouts, savoys, brocoli, and leeks; thin parsnips, carrots, turnips, and beet; plant out celery for succession and for main crop; sow peas and beans for late crops, and nip off the tops of luxuriant beans coming into flower; sow scarlet runners, kidney beans, white stone, and other turnips; plant out vegetable marrow; ridge cucumbers and tomatoes; apply liquid manure to cauliflowers, early peas, &c., which are required in perfection at an early period, frequently stirring the soil to give free admission to sun and air. Dull, showery weather will be best suited for the pricking out of young plants into beds. Furnish peas of early sowings with stakes as soon as they are a few inches above ground.

JULY.

FRUITS.—Protect young shoots of fruit trees grafted in spring, as they are liable to split off in severe weather; clear away all suckers from fruit trees, as their growth will damage the fruit and prevent them from coming to perfection. They must not be cut merely with the level of the ground, but traced to their origin, and carefully removed with the point of a sharp knife. Prepare the ground for new plantations of strawberries; the earliest plants produced by this year's runners are best, and should have a deep rich soil, with abundance of manure. Cherries and plums may be bedded same as roses; trim hedges and evergreens, and guard against greenfly and mildew, so destructive to roses.

FLOWERS.—Proceed with the budding of roses in dark, showery weather, removing all suckers from the summer-flowering varieties; propagate pinks, carnations, &c., by layers and pipings, after which other hardy plants, such as wall-flowers, phloxes, pansies, &c., should be attended to; make a small sowing of the more hardy annuals for autumn flowering; clear away all decaying bloom, and keep edgings and walks clean and tidy.

VEGETABLES.—Make a sowing of peas for last crop, and prepare a piece of ground for winter spinach; sow early York cabbage for transplanting, also brocoli and parsley for winter supply, and a few horn carrots for drawing young in autumn; stake peas and scarlet runners, and sow the last crop of kidney beans in the first few days of the month. Plant celery in shallow trenches, and keep it earthed up as it advances in growth; take up garlic, shallots, and onions, and tie in bunches, hanging them in a dry, airy place; remove weakly shoots, &c., from cucumbers, and keep them well watered.

AUGUST.

FRUITS.—If a sufficient number of young strawberry plants have been obtained, all the runners should be cleared away from the old plants, and a quantity of decomposed manure forked about the roots, care being taken not to injure the foliage. This will encourage a more prolific yield during the remainder of the season, and keep the plants in a healthy state for next season's crop. Protect ripening plums and other wall fruit from the ravages of wasps, flies, &c. ; gather in the early varieties of apples and pears ; net up gooseberry and currant bushes in dry weather, to preserve the fruit till late autumn ; examine the ground about the roots of peaches and apricots on the open wall, particularly where copings are employed, and where found dry give a regular watering ; attend to grafts as last month ; remove weak and straggling offsets of vines, and thin out the smaller berries from bunches of grapes, which will increase the size of the remaining fruit.

FLOWERS.—Polyanthuses and auriculas may now be divided, replanted, or repotted. Cuttings of roses should be taken immediately and planted in a close, cool frame. In the beginning of the month carnations and picotés may be layered, and the better kinds shifted into pots as soon as they have rooted, so as to enable them to be more easily protected from frost. All tall-growing plants should be properly staked and tied, and well watered in dry weather, adding a little liquid manure to plants that may appear weak or sickly. Dahlias must have a plentiful supply of water, and be well mulched with rotted manure. The second crop of pink pipings may be planted out, and the beds should be examined in the evenings to guard against worms, which often make great havoc among the stocks ; remove all decayed leaves and blossoms from flower beds, and hoe, rake, and roll walks.

VEGETABLES.—Two sowings of cauliflowers may be made, one at the beginning and one towards the end of the month. Varieties of lettuce, of the hardy kinds, should be sown by the end of the month, and covered with glass in autumn and winter. Sow main crop of winter spinach, on rich ground, well manured and deeply trenched ; continue the earthing up of celery, bend down the necks of onions, and sow endive, winter lettuce, prickly spinage, and small salads ; prepare a bed for sowing cabbage for spring and summer supply ; hoe frequently between young plants of Brussels sprouts, Savoys, &c. ; take up and dry garlic, shallots, and onions, as they ripen ; lift the early kinds of potatoes, and carefully sort the produce, laying past medium-sized tubers in dry sand or charcoal dust ; secure an ample supply of salads for winter use.

SEPTEMBER.

FRUITS.—Young plantations of strawberries should be carefully looked after, and the soil between the plants slightly stirred, adding a liberal supply of liquid manure, which will be repaid with an abundant crop next year. Cut old raspberry canes, and reduce the young saplings to whatever number it is intended to keep. Wall trees should be carefully gone over, and all extra growth pinched back to prevent excess of useless wood tended to injure weak branches. Gather apples, pears, plums, &c., as they ripen. [To tell whether fruit is thoroughly ripe for picking, raise it gently with the hand, when the stalk will leave the tree at once if it is in fit condition]. Rooted runners of strawberries may still be planted in lines or beds ; store onions as soon as ripe ; carefully dry them in the shade, if possible, and then store them in a dry and frost-proof place.

FLOWERS.—Every exertion should be made to get cuttings struck while genial weather lasts, so that they may become fairly established and properly rooted before winter, as nothing is more desirable than well-rooted cuttings when the time comes for planting out. Even those who have not the privilege of a garden may at this season provide themselves with a variety of cuttings, which will grow to perfection in any light soil, well mixed with sand. Plant hyacinths, tulips, and crocuses in beds or borders for early flowering, and plant a few of the very early sorts in pots for forcing ;

take up lilies as the foliage decays, and dry them gradually; see that gladioli and other tall-growing plants are properly staked; stake and tie the young shoots of budded roses, to secure them from strong winds; put in cuttings of China or monthly roses; transplant, prune, and train evergreens and climbers, and look to edgings of box, &c. All alterations or improvements should be commenced at once, as any fresh shrubs planted will have time to take root before winter.

VEGETABLES.—Any early potatoes remaining in the ground should be removed, and all diseased tubers carefully extracted. Those intended for seed ought to be dried in the sun, and, after being sprinkled with quicklime or dry mould, should be put past in a dry, cool place, and well guarded from frost. Sow the last crops of winter spinage, lettuces, radishes, and small salads, without delay, and continue to plant for succession cauliflower, cabbage, borecole, savoy, &c.; earth up former plantations as they advance; thin out turnips, winter spinage, and all crops that are sufficiently forward; hoe weeds from all parts of the garden, and remove all kinds of decaying or useless vegetation; take up and dry onions, and clean and store them.

OCTOBER.

FRUITS.—The general crop of apples, pears, &c., are now ripe, and should be gathered, picking out all damaged fruit for immediate use, as, if stored past with the sound ones, they will soon show symptoms of decay, and will damage the healthy fruit that may come in contact with them. This month will be found most desirable for transplanting and pruning the roots of fruit bushes, as any planted prior to the end of December will have a decided advantage over those which may be deferred till a later period. If assisted by mulching with short manure they will only require a very brief season of repose. The depth of the soil should not in any case exceed eighteen inches, and where it is damp should be made above the ordinary level for choice fruit trees, such as apricots, peaches, &c. If propagation is desired, the strongest shoots should invariably be laid, and a coating of lime round the stem will protect from caterpillars.

FLOWERS.—As the cold weather will soon set in, all summer flowers must be removed from the beds and re-potted, and the beds neatly forked over. The bulbs of dahlias should be taken up, slightly dried, and stored beyond the reach of frost. About the end of the month hardy annuals may be sown, as they will survive the winter and flower early in spring; crocuses, snowdrops, &c., may also be planted. The greatest attention will be necessary in repairing and making up the walks, filling up all hollows to prevent an accumulation of water. As the enjoyment of the garden during the winter greatly depends on the dryness and tidy appearance of the walks, the falling leaves must be cleared away daily, so as to prevent that unsightly appearance which, if allowed to remain, they are sure to produce. Unoccupied soil should be dug up and exposed to the coming frosts, which will purify and make it more productive.

VEGETABLES.—Most of the root crops, such as potatoes, parsnips, carrots, and beet, may now be lifted and stored past, selecting dry weather for this operation. Earth up celery, and plant out cabbages for spring use, and lettuces in warm borders. It will be found most advantageous to clear away all weeds, so that none may be allowed to seed and cause double trouble next year. Thin out the late crops of turnips, spinach, &c., and stir up the soil between the rows. The wet days may be turned to advantage in hanking the onions and putting them in a secure place, and in picking out all diseased potatoes from amongst those intended for immediate use or for seed.

NOVEMBER.

FRUITS.—Wall trees will now require a share of attention, as the operation of training can be performed with more ease, and with greater advantage to the trees early in the season. The pruning and transplanting of apples, pears, plums, cherries, gooseberries, currants, raspberries, and all kinds of fruit trees should be proceeded with, and newly-planted trees, of a tender kind, should be well protected against frost, and have some rotted manure forked round the roots. As the pruning is completed the ground should be left in a rough state, to be subject to the action of the winter's frost.

FLOWERS.—Perfect neatness should now claim attention in every department of the flower garden. Remove all fallen leaves, and slightly fork over or rake the borders. The walks must be got into perfect trim, and gravelled where necessary. Examine dahlia roots, and, if free from mouldiness, store away in a moderately dry place; climbing plants and flowering shrubs may now be obtained and planted; plant hyacinths and tulips early in the month—the first week, if possible—for spring flowering; watch any plants that may be in pits, giving them light and air freely on the milder days of the month, carefully covering them again as soon as the sun goes down; protect roses not thoroughly hardy with mats, or other suitable covering.

VEGETABLES.—Protect pits and frames containing young cauliflower and lettuce plants in severe weather; trench and ridge up all ground as rapidly as it becomes vacant, leaving it in a rough state; cart out any necessary manure during frosty weather, and make it in large heaps, to be used as required; cover over the crowns of rhubarb and seakale with dry dung, sand, or some similar material. A sowing of early beans and peas may now be made, on well-manured ground, in a warm, sheltered border.

DECEMBER.

FRUITS.—Great care must be taken to protect against frost in every department, but as little else can be done in this month, save attending to the walks and preparing soils and manure for next spring, the greater portion of the time can be given to this object. Turf sods or willow dust for auriculas, cow manure for ranunculuses, and stable manure for carnations and picotés, should be provided. Mulch over the roots of tender trees, such as apricot and peach, as they are often so far affected by frost as to be barren in the coming year. In mild weather transplant hardy fruit trees, but not too deep.

FLOWERS.—The flower garden has now lost all its attractiveness, and has the appearance of a bleak waste; but this must not be an excuse for neglect. The clearing away of fallen and decaying foliage must be attended to, and the walks kept clean and tidy—in fact, everything must be done to make up in neatness what is wanted in beauty. A few hollyhock rooted cuttings or seedlings may be planted out in mild weather; cover hyacinth and tulip beds with mats or other covering to protect from frost, and give protection to flowering shrubs, roses, &c., not thoroughly hardy; remove the covering in mild, sunny days; lay off flower-beds, and carry out any necessary ground alterations in favourable weather.

VEGETABLES.—Let the trenching and manuring of vacant ground be proceeded with in dry weather. Attend to the forcing of rhubarb, seakale, and asparagus, which may be accomplished in the open ground by putting tall pots over the crowns, and covering them with stable litter or leaves, to keep up a gentle heat. As mentioned last month, take advantage of frosty weather to collect manure to spots intended for spring cropping. Make another sowing of early peas and beans, and plant kidney-shaped potatoes, on a sheltered border, and protect with litter if frost sets in.

FAIRS IN ULSTER FOR 1880.

NOTE.—So many alterations taking place during the year, relative to fairs held on Saturdays and those falling on a Sunday, which we publish as on that day, parties wishing to attend are advised to inquire from some responsible authority in the locality on the subject, as we cannot be accountable for such errors, some holding on the Monday following, and others on the day preceding.

JANUARY.

Th. 1 Antrim town
Ardara, don
Armagh town
Ballinanagh, cavan
Ballyliffin, don
Belleek, fer
Belturbet, cavan
Carrickmaquigley, don
Carrowkeel, don
Feeny, derry
Kilmacrenan, don
Middletown, arm
Redcastle, don
Redhill, cav
Strabane, tyr
Fri. 2 Ballyconnell, cavan
Ballyshannon, don
Cross, derry
Crossmaglen, arm
Draperstown, derry
Fivemiletown, tyr
Mahoolan, derry
Moy, tyr
Sat. 3 Clogher, tyr
Cookstown, tyr
Dawra, cavan
Dromore, down
Frederickstown, tyr
Lisnaskea, fer
Poyntzpass, arm
Stranorlar, don
Sun. 4 Mounthamilton, tyr
Mon. 5 Altmore, tyr
Ballybot, arm
Banbridge, down
Bailieborough, cavan
Bawnboy, cavan
Blownrock, don
Belcoo or Hollywell, fer
Bellaghy, derry
Beragh, tyr
Castlefin, don
Crumlin, ant

Dromore, tyr
Dungloe, don
Kesh, fer
Kirkcubbin, down
Monaghan town
Tu. 6 Crosskeys, cav
Coleraine, derry
Donaghmore, tyr
Downpatrick, down
Dunfanaghy, don
Gortahook, don
Kingscourt, cavan
Omagh, tyr
Portglenone, ant
Seaford, down
Wed. 7 Aughnacloy, tyr
Ballow, down
Belfast, ant
Castleblayney, mon
Gortin, tyr
Killeshandra, cavan
Londonderry city
Maguiresbridge, fer
Rathfriland, down
Rossnakill, don
Thur. 8 Ballybofey, don
Carrickmacross, mon
Irvinestown, fer
Kells, ant
Kerrykeel, don
Largymore, don
Larne, ant
Lurgan, arm
Roslea, fer
Fr. 9 Ballygawley, tyr
Coagh, tyr
Donegal town
Keady, arm
Sat. 10 Caledon, tyr
Creeslagh, don
Enniskillen, fer
Newtownards, down
Richhill, arm
Mo. 12 Aghygaults, don

Ballycarry, ant
Banbridge, down
Bangor, down
Castlecaulfield, tyr
Castlewellan, down
Dervock, ant
Greencastle, down
Lisburn, ant
Mountnorris, arm
Seskinore, tyr
Surgowney, arm
Tubbermore, derry
Tu. 13 Ballycastle, ant
Cavan town
Cullybanna, arm
Dungiven, derry
Hilltown, down
Portaferry, down
Pomeroy, tyr
Wed. 14 Crossroads, don
Crossgar, down
Glen, don
Kilrea, derry
Shircock, cavan
Stewartstown, tyr
Tanderagee, arm
Trillick, tyr
Thu. 15 Bernice, ant
Ballynahinch, down
Comber, down
Laghey, don
Ramelton, don
Rathmullan, don
Fr. 16 Bundoran, don
Cootehill, cavan
Carrick, don
Dunkaneely, don
Garvagh, derry
Glasslough, mon
Killybegs, don
Markethill, arm
Plumbridge, tyr
Sat. 17 Ballybay, mon
Claudy, derry
Ederneybridge, fer

Kilgolagh, cavan
Maguiresbridge, fer
Portadown, arm
Raphoe, don
Scotstown, mon
  Mo. 19 Camlough,arm
Churchhill, don
Killen, tyr
Swateragh, derry
Sixmilecross, tyr
  Tu. 20 Ballinacarrick,
  don
Cranagh, tyr
Dundrum, down
Glenties, don
Pettigo, don
Rostrevor, down
  Wed. 21 Ballinanagh,
  cavan
Hillsborough, down
Killetter, tyr
Moneymore, derry
  Th. 22 Blacklion, cav
Fintona, tyr
Mountcharles, don
  Fri. 23 Milford, don
Newtownards, down
  Sat. 24 Derrygonnelly,
  fer
Tydavnet, mon
Virginia, cavan
  Mon. 26 Armoy, ant
Ballintra, don
Derrybeg, don
Glenarm, ant
Kilcar, don
Newtownstewart, tyr
Rock, tyr
  Tu. 27 Ballyclare, ant
Bushmills, ant
Carrickmore, tyr
Donemana, tyr
Maghera, derry
  Wed. 28 Benburb, tyr
Kilkeel, down
Saintfield, down
Tempo, fer
  Th. 29 Antrim town
Crossroads, don
Clones, mon
Drumquin, tyr
Magherafelt, derry
Manorcunningham, don
Moville, don
  Fr. 30 Arvagh, cavan
Ballymena, antrim

Castlederg, tyr
Killyleagh, arm
Lack, fer
Letterkerny, don
Mullagh, cavan
Warrenpoint, down
  Sa. 31 Clabby, fer
Castledawson, derry
Maghery, arm
Newtownhamilton, arm

FEBRUARY.

  Sun. 1 Tullyodonald,
  don
  Mon. 2 Ardara, don
Altmore, tyr
Bailieborough, cavan
Banbridge, down
Ballybot, arm
Ballyshannon, don
Bawnboy, cavan
Bellaghy, derry
Beragh, tyr
Brockagh, don
Castlewellan, down
Clady, tyr
Cloghanbeg, don
Connor, ant
Crumlin, ant
Dromore, tyr
Hollywood, down
Kilnaleck, cavan
Kilmacrenan, don
Kirkcubbin, down
Monaghan town
Swanlinbar, cavan
Strabane, tyr
  Tu. 3 Burnfoot, don
Coleraine, derry
Dawra, cavan
Donaghmore, tyr
Downpatrick, down
Gortahook, don
Kingscourt, cavan
Omagh, tyr
Portglenone, ant
Seaford, down
  We. 4 Aughnacloy, tyr
Ballyjamesduff, cavan
Belfast, ant
Castleblayney, mon
Cushendun, ant
Desertmartin, derry
Dungloe, don
Gortin, tyr
Kesh, fer

Killeshandra, cavan
Londonderry city
Maguiresbridge, fer
Rathfriland, down
Rosnakill, don
  Th. 5 Armagh town
Belcoo or Hollywell, fer
Belturbet, cav
Blownrock, don
Dungloe, don
Greencastle, don
Kilcoguy, cavan
Middletown, arm
Moira, down
Muff, derry
Newtowncrumlin, ant
  Fri. 6 Crossmaglen,
  arm
Cross, derry
Draperstown, derry
Dromara, down
Dunfanaghy, don
Fivemiletown, tyr
Mahoolan, derry
Moy, tyr
Sheepbridge, down
  Sa. 7 Caradore, down
Clogher, tyrone
Cookstown, tyr
Dromore, down
Lisnaskea, fer
Parkgate, ant
Poyntzpass, arm
Stradone, cavan
Stranorlar, don
  Sun. 8 Derrylin, fer
  Mon. 9 Castlefin, don
Castlecaulfield, tyr
Irvinestown, fer
Kerrykeel, don
Limavady, derry
Lisburn, antrim
Mountnorris, arm
Roslea, fer
Seskinore, tyr
Tubbermore, derry
  Tu. 10 Ballycastle, ant
Carnlough, ant
Cavan town
Creeslagh, don
Culdaff, don
Dungiven, derry
Enniskillen, fer
Hilltown, down
Kilcar, don
Monea, fer

Pomeroy, tyr
Portaferry, down
Wed. 11 Belturbet, cav
Crossgar, down
Kilrea, derry
Larne, ant
Portnorris, arm
Shircock, cavan
Tanderagee, arm
Th. 12 Ballybofey, don
Carrickmacross, mon
Churchtown, derry
Lurgan, arm
Fri. 13 Ballyconnell, cavan
Ballygawley, tyr
Coagh, tyr
Donegal town
Keady, arm
Mosside, ant
Sa. 14 Cushendall, ant
Caledon, tyr
Carrickmaquigley, don
Glen, don
Newtownards, down
Raphoe, don
Richhill, arm
Trillick, tyrone
Virginia, cavan
Sun. 15 Laghy, don
Ramelton, don
Mo. 16 Bundoran, don
Camlough, arm
Dunkineely, don
Dunloy, ant
Plumbridge, tyr
Swateragh, derry
Tu. 17 Claudy, derry
Dundrum, down
Ederneybridge, fer
Glenties, don
Rostrevor, down
Scotstown, mon
Wed. 18 Churchhill, don
Hillsborough, down
Stewartstown, tyr
Th. 19 Bernice, ant
Ballynahinch, down
Loughgill, antrim
Rathmullan, don
Sixmilecross, tyr
Fri. 20 Ballinacarrick, don
Cootehill, cav
Cranagh, tyr

Garvagh, Derry
Glasslough, mon
Markethill, arm
Pettigo, don
Sat. 21 Ballybay, mon
Carndonagh, don
Killetter, tyr
Moneymore, derry
Portadown, arm
Mo. 23 Blacklion, cav
Carrick, don
Dervock, ant
Derrybeg, don
Fintona, tyr
Milford, don
Mountcharles, don
Newtownstewart, tyr
Rock, tyr
Tu. 24 Ballintra, don
Bushmills, ant
Carrickmore, tyr
Derrygonnelly, fer
Grousehall, don
Maghera, derry
Tydavnet, mon
Wed. 25 Armoy, ant
Benburb, tyr
Glenoe, ant
Kilkeel, down
Saintfield, down
Th. 26 Antrim town
Clones, mon
Crossroads, don
Drumquin, tyr
Magherafelt, derry
Manorcunningham, don
Moville, don
Fri. 27 Ballymena, ant
Castlederg, tyr
Donemana, tyr
Killyleagh, arm
Lack, fer
Mullagh, cavan
Termonrock, tyr
Warrenpoint, down
Sa. 28 Castledawson, derry
N:townhamiltown, arm
Tempo, fer

MARCH.

Mo. 1 Ardara, don
Altmore, tyr
Ballybot, arm
Bailieborough, cavan
Ballyhays, cavan

Banbridge, down
Bawnboy, cavan
Bellaghy, derry
Beragh, tyr
Crumlin, ant
Dromore, tyr
Kells, ant
Kilmacrenan, don
Kirkcubbin, down
Monaghan town
Tu. 2 Coleraine, derry
Ballyshannon, don
Donaghmore, tyr
Downpatrick, down
Gortahook, don
Kingscourt, cavan
Omagh, tyr
Portglenone, ant
Seaford, down
We. 3 Aughnacloy, tyr
Belfast, ant
Castleblayney, mon
Dawra, cavan
Frederickstown, tyr
Gortin, tyr
Londonderry city
Maguiresbridge, fer
Rathfriland, down
Rosnakill, don
Th. 4 Armagh town
Belturbet, cavan
Dungloe, don
Kesh, fer
Middletown, arm
Strabane, tyr
Fri. 5 Blownrock, don
Belcoo or Hollywell, fer
Crossmaglen, arm
Cross, derry
Draperstown, derry
Fivemiletown, tyr
Mahoolan, derry
Moy, tyrone
Sa. 6 Clogher, tyr
Cookstown, tyr
Dunfanaghy, don
Dromore, down
Lisnaskea, fer
Pointzpass, arm
Virginia, cavan
Stranorlar, don
Mo 8 Ballyjamesduff, cavan
Castlewellan, down
Castlecaulfield, tyr
Irvinestown, fer

Kerrykeel, don
Limavady, derry
Lisburn, ant
Mountnorris, arm
Roslea, fer
Seskinore, tyr
Tubbermore, derry
Tu. 9 Ballycastle, ant
Cavan town
Dungiven, derry
Hilltown, down
Portaferry, down
Pomeroy, tyr
Wed. 10 Crossgar, down
Creeslagh, don
Enniskillen, fer
Kilrea, derry
Shircock, cavan
Tanderagee, arm
Th. 11 Ballybofey, don
Carrickmacross, mon
Larne, ant
Lurgan, arm
Fri. 12 Donegal town
Ballygawley, tyr
Coagh, tyr
Keady, arm
Letterkenny, don
Sa. 13 Caledon, tyr
Carrickmaquigley, don
Newtownards, down
Raphoe, don
Richhill, armagh
Mo. 15 Claudy, derry
Camlough, arm
Glen, don
Laghey, don
Ramelton, don
Swateragh, derry
Trillick, tyr
Tu. 16 Bundoran, don
Dundrum, down
Dunkineely, don
Plumbridge, tyr
Rostrevor, down
We. 17 Ballyconnell, cavan
Ballytrain, mon
Belleek, fer
Cushendall, ant
Crosskeys, cavan
Castlefin, don
Ederneybridge, fer
Feeny, derry
Glenties, don
Hillsborough, down

Scotstown, mon
Stewartstown, tyr
Th. 18 Ballynahinch, down
Churchhill, don
Rathmullan, don
Fr. 19 Cootehill, cavan
Garvagh, Derry
Glasslough, mon
Markethill, arm
Sixmilecross, tyr
Sa. 20 Aghygaults, don
Ballybay, mon
Cranagh, tyr
Dromara, down
Portadown, armagh
Pettigo, don
Mo. 22 Blacklion, cav
Fintona, tyr
Killeter, tyr
Mountcharles, don
Moneymore, derry
Scarva, down
Tu. 23 Milford, don
We. 24 Ballintra, don
Derrygonnelly, fer
Tydavnet, mon
Th. 25 Arvagh, cavan
Antrim town
Ballinagh, cavan
Clones, mon
Crossroads, don
Drumquin, tyr
Kilnaleck, cavan
Letterkenny, don
Manorcunningham, don
Moville, don
Magherafelt, derry
Fr. 26 Arvagh, cavan
Ballymena, ant
Castlederg, tyr
Killyleagh, arm
Lack, fer
Mullagh, cavan
Termonrock, tyr
Warrenpoint, down
Sa. 27 Carrowkeel, don
Castledawson, derry
Donemana, tyr
Newtownhamilton, arm
Virginia, cavan
Sun. 28 Armoy, ant
Mo. 29 Ballyliffin, don
Carnlough, ant
Castlefin, don
Callowhill, fer

Derrybeg, don
Killeshandra, cavan
Killybegs, don
Newtownstewart, tyr
Portadown, arm
Rock, tyr
Stradone, cavan
Toome, ant
Tempo, fer
Tu. 30 Ballycastle, ant
Bushmills, ant
Carrickmore, tyr
Maghera, derry
Swanlinbar, cavan
We. 31 Benburb, tyr
Kilkeel, down
Killygordon, don
Saintfield, down

APRIL.

Th. 1 Ardara, don
Altmore, tyr
Armagh town
Belturbet, cavan
Kilmacrenan, don
Middletown, arm
Strabane, tyr
Fr. 2 Ballyshannon, don
Cross, derry
Crossmaglen, arm
Draperstown, derry
Fivemiletown, tyr
Mahoolan, derry
Moy, tyr
Sa. 3 Clogher, tyr
Cookstown, tyr
Dawra, cavan
Dromore, down
Lisnaskea, fer
Poyntzpass, arm
Stranorlar, don
Mo. 5 Ballybot, arm
Bailieborough, cavan
Bawnboy, cavan
Blownrock, don
Banbridge, down
Belcoo or Hollywell, fer
Bellaghy, derry
Beragh, tyr
Crumlin, ant
Crossdowney, cavan
Comber, down
Dungloe, don
Dromore, tyr
Kesh, fer

Monaghan town
Mountnorris, arm
  Tu. 6 Coleraine, derry
Donaghmore, tyr
Downpatrick, down
Dromore West, tyr
Dunfanaghy, don
Gortahook, don
Kingscourt, cavan
Omagh, tyr
Portglenone, ant
Seaford, down
  We. 7 Aughnacloy, tyr
Belfast, ant
Castleblayney, mon
Cushendun, ant
Gortin, tyr
Londonderry city
Maguiresbridge, fer
Rathfriland, down
Rosnakill, don
  Th. 8 Ballybofey, don
Belturbet, cavan
Carrickmacross, mon
Irvinestown, fer
Kerrykeel, don
Larne, ant
Lurgan, arm
Roslea, fer
  Fr. 9 Ballygawley, tyr
Coagh, tyr
Donegal town
Keady, arm
  Sa. 10 Caledon, tyr
Creeslagh, don
Enniskillen, fer
Newtownards, down
Richhill, arm
  Mo. 12 Ballyhays, cav
Castlecaulfield, tyr
Castlewellan, down
Killileagh, down
Lisburn, antrim
Seskinore, tyr
Tubbermore, derry
  Tu. 13 Ballycastle, ant
Cavan town
Cullyhanna, arm
Dungiven, derry
Hilltown, down
Portaferry, down
Pomeroy, tyr
  Wed. 14 Arvagh, cavan
Carrick, don
Crossgar, down
Glen, don

Kilrea, derry
Shircock, cavan
Stewartstown, tyr
Tanderagee, arm
Trillick, tyr
  Th. 15 Ballynahinch,
    down
Laghy, don
Ramelton, don
Rathmullan, don
  Fri. 16 Bundoran, don
Ballyjamesduff, cavan
Cootehill, cavan
Dunkineely, don
Garvagh, derry
Glasslough, mon
Markethill, arm
Plumbridge, tyr
  Sa. 17 Ballybay, mon
Carrickmaquigley, don
Claudy, derry
Ederneybridge, fer
Portadown, arm
Raphoe, don
Scotstown, mon
  Mo. 19 Ballycarry, ant
Ballyconnell, cavan
Camlough, arm
Churchhill, don
Sixmilecross, tyr
Swateragh, derry
  Tu. 20 Ballinacarrick,
    don
Carrowkeel, don
Cranagh, tyr
Dundrum, down
Pettigo, don
Rostrevor, down
  We. 21 Glenties, don
Hillsborough, down
Killetter, tyr
Moneymore, derry
  Th. 22 Blacklion, cav
Fintona, tyr
Mountcharles, don
  Fr. 23 Milford, don
  Sa. 24 Castledawson,
    derry
Derrygonnelly, fer
Newtownhamilton, arm
Tydavnet, mon
  Mon. 26 Ballintra, don
Derrybeg, don
Kilcar, don
Newtownstewart, tyr
Rock, tyr

  Tu. 27 Bushmills, ant
Carrickmore, tyr
Donemana, tyr
Maghera, derry
  We. 28 Benburb, tyr
Kirkcubbin, down
Saintfield, down
Tempo, fer
  Th. 29 Antrim town
Crossroads, don
Clones, mon
Drumquin, tyr
Grayabbey, down
Magherafelt, derry
Manorcunningham, don
Moville, don
  Fr. 30 Ballymena, ant
Castlederg, tyr
Killyleagh, arm
Lack, fer
Maghery, arm
Mullogh, cavan
Termonrock, tyr
Warrenpoint, down

MAY.

  Sa. 1 Ardara, don
Arvagh, cavan
Ballytrain, mon
Bangor, down
Castlewellan, down
Clogher, tyr
Cookstown, tyr
Connor, ant
Dromara, down
Dromore, down
Feeny, derry
Forkhill, arm
Glenoe, ant
Killinchy, down
Kilmacrenan, don
Lisnaskea, fer
Mountnugent, cavan
Newtownsaville, tyr
Raphoe, don
Stranorlar, don
  Sun. 2 Ards-trawbridge,
    tyr
Ballyshannon, don
  Mo. 3 Altmore, tyr
Bailieborough, cavan
Ballybot, arm
Banbridge, down
Bawnboy, cavan
Bellaghy, derry
Beragh, tyr

Crumlin, ant
Dawra, cavan
Dromore, tyr
Hollywood, down
Monaghan town
   Tu. 4 Burnfoot, don
Coleraine, derry
Dungloe, don
Donaghmore, tyr
Downpatrick, down
Gortahook, don
Kingscourt, cavan
Kesh, fer
Omagh, tyr
Portglenone, ant
Tullivin, cavan
Seaford, down
   We. 5 Aughnacloy, tyr
Ballinanagh, cavan
Ballymoney, ant
Belcoo or Hollywell, fer
Belfast, ant
Blownrock, don
Castleblayney, mon
Gortin, tyr
Greencastle, don
Londonderry city
Maguiresbridge, fer
Rathfriland, down
Rosnakill, don
Tanderagee, arm
   Th. 6 Armagh town
Belturbet, cavan
Dunfanaghy, don
Killybegs, don
Machrecregan, tyr
Middletown, arm
Moira, down
Muff, derry
Scrabby, cavan
   Fr. 7 Ballyjamesduff, cavan
Cross, derry
Crossmaglen, arm
Draperstown, derry
Fivemiletown, tyr
Mahoolan, derry
Moy, tyr
Parkgate, ant
Sheepbridge, down
   Sa. 8 Caledon, tyr
Caradore, down
Desertmartin, derry
Glenties, don
Irvinestown, fer
Kerrykeel, don

Largymore, don
Newtownards, down
Poyntzpass, arm
Richhill, arm
Rosslea, fer
   Mon. 10 Creeslagh, don
Culdaff, don
Castlecaulfield, tyr
Enniskillen, fer
Killeshandra, cavan
Lisburn, ant
Mountnorris, arm
Seskinore, tyr
Stradone, cavan
Tubbermore, derry
   Tu. 11 Ballycastle, ant
Dungiven, derry
Hilltown, down
Lisbellaw, fer
Portaferry, down
Pomeroy, tyr
Virginia, cavan
   Wed. 12 Antrim town
Augher, tyr
Carrickfergus, ant
Crossgar, down
Coleraine, derry
Dromore, down
Kilrea, derry
Letterkenny, don
Lislane, derry
Newtownbutler, fer
Newtowncrumlin, ant
Portnorris, arm
Shircock, cavan
Strabane, tyr
Straid, ant
Tanderagee, arm
   Th. 13 Kilnaleck, cavan
Charlemount, arm
Larne, ant
Lurgan, arm
Port, don
Wheathill, fer
   Fr. 14 Ballygawley, tyr
Cushendall, ant
Cavan town
Churchhill, fer
Coagh, tyr
Donegal town
Glen, don
Keady, arm
Newtownards, down
Surgowney, arm
Trillick, tyr
   Sa. 15 Aghygaults, don

Ballybay, mon
Buncrana, don
Churchtown, derry
Dunloy, ant
Laghy, don
Ramelton, don
Portadown, arm
   Sun. 16 Bundoran, don
   Mo. 17 Belleek, fer
Ballyconnell, cavan
Clady, tyr
Camlough, arm
Carrick, don
Castlefin, don
Claudy, derry
Convoy, don
Dervock, ant
Dunkaneely, don
Ederneybridge, fer
Fintown, don
Plumbridge, tyr
Portadown, arm
Swatteragh, derry
Scotstown, mon
Tullyodonald, don
   Tu. 18 Ballyhays, cav
Carnmoney, ant
Churchhill, don
Dundrum, down
Rosstrevor, down
Swanlinbar, cavan
   We. 19 Brockagh, don
Cloghanbeg, don
Hillsborough, down
Maguiresbridge, fer
Sixmilecross, tyr
Stewartstown, tyr
   Th. 20 Ballinacarrick, don
Ballynabinch, down
Cranagh, tyr
Killen, tyr
Pettigo, don
Rathmullan, don
   Fri. 21 Ballybofey, don
Cootehill, cav
Carndonagh, don
Clough, down
Garrison, fer
Garvagh, derry
Glasslough, mon
Killetter, tyr
Markethill, arm
Moneymore, derry
Mosside, ant
   Sa. 22 Blacklion, cav

Fintona, tyr
Mountcharles, don
Mo. 24 Ballintra, don
Ballymagauran, cavan
Derrygonnelly, fer
Milford, don
Redhills, cavan
Tydavnet, mon
Tu. 25 Armoy, ant
Ballycastle, ant
Ballyclare, ant
Bushmills, ant
Carrickmore, tyr
Clabby, fer
Grousehall, don
Kilcogny, cavan
Maghera, derry
Portglenone, ant
We. 26 Benburb, tyr
Derrylin, fer
Donaghadee, down
Enniskillen, fer
Glenarm, ant
Hamiltonsbawn, arm
Kilkeel, down
Saintfield, down
Th. 27 Antrim town
Ballsmill, arm
Carrowkeel, don
Clough, ant
Crossdowney, cavan
Crossroads, don
Carrickmacross, mon
Clones, mon
Donemana, tyr
Drumquin, tyr
Magherafelt, derry
Manorcunningham, don
Moville, don
Fri. 28 Ballymena, ant
Castlederg, tyr
Killyleagh, arm
Kirkcubbin, down
Lack, fer
Mullagh, cavan
Tempo, fer
Termonrock, tyr
Warrenpoint, down
Sa. 29 Castledawson, derry
Newtownhamilton, arm
Mo. 31 Derrybeg, don
Killygordon, don
Newtownstewart, tyr
Rock, tyr
Straid, ant

JUNE.
Tu. 1 Ardara, don
Carrickmaquigley, don
Castlewellan, down
Coleraine, derry
Donaghmore, tyr
Downpatrick, down
Kingscourt, cavan
Kilmacrenan, don
Mountnugent, cavan
Omagh, tyr
Portglenone, ant
Redcastle, don
Rockfort, ant
Stragowna, fer
We. 2 Aughnacloy, tyr
Belfast, ant
Ballyshannon, don
Castleblayney, mon
Cushendun, ant
Gortin, tyr
Londonderry city
Maguiresbridge, fer
Rathfriland, down
Th. 3 Armagh town
Ballintoy, ant
Belturbet, cavan
Dawra, cavan
Frederickstown, tyr
Strabane, tyr
Virginia, cavan
Fr. 4 Ahoghill, ant
Crossmaglen, arm
Cross, derry
Dungloe, don
Draperstown, derry
Fivemiletown, tyrone
Kesh, fer
Mahoolan, derry
Mounthamilton, tyr
Moy, tyr
Sat. 5 Ballinanagh, cavan
Belcoo or Hollywell, fer
Blownrock, don
Clogher, tyr
Cookstown, tyr
Dromore, down
Kilcar, don
Lisnaskea, fer
Poyntzpass, arm
Straorlar, don
Mo. 7 Altmore, tyr
Bailieborough, cavan
Ball bot, arm
Banbridge, down

Bawnboy, cavan
Bellaghy, derry
Beragh, tyr
Crumlin, ant
Desertmartin, derry
Dromore, tyr
Dunfanaghy, don
Kirkcubbin, down
Monaghan town
Tu. 8 Arvagh, cavan
Ballycastle, ant
Cavan town
Dungiven, derry
Hilltown, down
Irvinestown, fer
Kerrykeel, don
Oldtown, don
Portaferry, down
Pomeroy, tyr
Roslea, fer
We. 9 Banbridge, down
Cloughmills, ant
Crossgar, down
Drumadoon, ant
Kilrea, derry
Shircock, cavan
Tanderagee, arm
Th. 10 Ballybofey, don
Ballyjamesduff, cavan
Creeslagh, don
Enniskillen, fer
Kells, ant
Larne, ant
Lurgan, arm
Monea, fer
Fri. 11 Ballygawley, tyr
Ballytrain, mon
Coagh, tyr
Donegal town
Keady, arm
Kilnaleck, cavan
Sa. 12 Caledon, tyr
Carnlough, ant
Gortahook, don
Newtownards, down
Mo. 14 Glen, don
Castlecaulfield, tyr
Lisburn, ant
Limavady, derry
Old-tone, ant
Tubbermore, derry
Trillick, tyr
Tu. 15 Claudy, derry
Dundrum, down
Laghey, don
Rostrevor, down

We. 16 Bundoran, don
Dunkineely, don
Hillsborough, down
Plumbridge, tyr
Stewartstown, tyr
Th. 17 Broughshane, ant
Ballynahinch, down
Ederneybridge, fer
Londonderry city
Rathmullan, don
Scotstown, mon
Fr. 18 Cootehill, cavan
Churchhill, don
Garvagh, derry
Glasslough, mon
Markethill, arm
Sa. 19 Ballybay, mon
Belleek, fer
Dromara, down
Glenties, don
Loughgyle, ant
Portadown, arm
Scarva, down
Sixmilecross, tyr
Sun. 20 Cranagh, tyr
Mo. 21 Ballyhays, cav
Camlough, arm
Killeter, tyr
Moneymore, derry
Park, derry
Pettigo, don
Swatteragh, derry
Tullyodonald, don
Tu. 22 Blacklion, cav
Ballywalter, down
Fintona, tyr
Killeshandra, cavan
Mountcharles, don
Raphoe, don
We. 23 Curran, derry
Greyabbey, down
Milford, don
Th. 24 Antrim town
Ballintra, don
Ballyconnell, cavan
Clones, mon
Crossroads, don
Derrygonnelly, fer
Drumquin, tyr
Feeny, derry
Maghery, arm
Malin, don
Magherafelt, derry
Manorcunningham, don
Moville, don

Stradone, cavan
Tydavnet, mon
Fr. 25 Ballymena, ant
Castlederg, tyr
Killyleagh, arm
Lack, fer
Mullogh, cavan
Termonrock, tyr
Warrenpoint, down
Sa. 26 Castledawson, derry
Craigbilly, ant
Killybegs, don
Newtownhamilton, arm
Mo. 28 Castlefin, don
Comber, down
Derrybeg, don
Donemana, tyr
Newtownstewart, tyr
Rock, tyr
Tempo, fer
Tu. 29 Bushmills, ant
Ballyliffin, don
Carrickmore, tyr
Cushendall, ant
Kilnaleck, cavan
Maghera, derry
Swanlinbar, cavan
We. 30 Benburb, tyr
Garrison, fer
Saintfield, down
Kilkeel, down

JULY.

Th. 1 Armagh town
Ardara, don
Belturbet, cavan
Kilmacrenan, don
Middletown, arm
Mounthill, ant
Strabane, tyr
Fr. 2 Ballyshannon, don
Cross, derry
Crossmaglen, arm
Draperstown, derry
Fivemiletown, tyr
Mahoolan, derry
Moy, tyr
Sa. 3 Clogher, tyr
Cookstown, tyr
Dawra, cavan
Dromore, down
Fintown, don
Lisnaskea, fer
Poyntzpass, arm

Mo. 5 Altmore, tyr
Bailieborough, cavan
Ballybot, arm
Banbridge, down
Bawnboy, cavan
Blownrock, don
Belcoo or Hollywell, fer
Bellaghy, derry
Beragh, tyr
Castlereagh, down
Crumlin, ant
Clough, down
Dungloe, don
Dromore, tyr
Kirkcubbin, down
Kesh, fer
Maguiresbridge, fer
Monaghan town
Stranorlar, don
Tanderagee, arm
Tu. 6 Coleraine, derry
Dunfanaghy, don
Donaghmore, tyr
Downpatrick, down
Kingscourt, cavan
Omagh, tyr
Portglenone, ant
Seaford, down
We. 7 Aughnacloy, tyr
Ballow, down
Belfast, ant
Castleblayney, mon
Gortin, tyr
Killeshandra, cavan
Londonderry city
Maguiresbridge, fer
Monea, fer
Rathfriland, down
Rossnakill, don
Th. 8 Ballybofey, don
Irvinestown, fer
Kerrykeel, don
Larne, antrim
Lurgan, arm
Roslea, fer
Fr. 9 Arvagh, cavan
Ballygawley, tyr
Clabby, fer
Coagh, tyr
Donegal town
Keady, arm
Virginia, cavan
Sat. 10 Ballymoney, ant
Caledon, tyr
Carrickmacross, mon
Creeslagh, don

Enniskillen, fer
Letterkenny, don
Newtownards, down
Orator, tyr
Richhill, arm
Templepatrick, ant
  Mo. 12 Castlecaulfield,
    tyr
Castlewellan, down
Limavady, derry
Mountnorris, arm
Seskinore, tyr
Tubbermore, derry
  Tu. 13 Ballycastle, ant
Ballyhays, cav
Cavan town
Dungiven, derry
Hilltown, down
Portaferry, down
Pomeroy, tyr
Wheathill, fer
  We. 14 Carrick, don
Crossgar, down
Glen, don
Kilrea, derry
Shircock, cavan
Stewartstown, tyr
Tanderagee, arm
Trillick, tyr
  Th. 15 Ballynahinch,
    down
Laghey, don
Ramelton, don
Rathmullan, don
  Fr. 16 Bundoran, don
Cootehill, cavan
Dunkaneely, don
Garvagh, derry
Glasslough, mon
Markethill, arm
Plumbridge, tyr
Randalstown, ant
  Sa. 17 Ballybay, mon
Ballyjamesduff, cavan
Claudy, derry
Ederneybridge, fer
Portadown, arm
Raphoe, don
Scotstown, mon
  Mo. 19 Camlough, arm
Churchhill, don
Garrison, fer
Killen, tyr
Sixmilecross, tyr
Swatteragh, derry
  Tu. 20 Aghygaults, don

Ballyclare, ant
Cranagh, tyr
Dundrum, down
Pettigo, don
Rostrevor, down
  We. 21 Killeter, tyr
Hillsborough, down
Lisburn, ant
Moneymore, derry
Mosside, ant
  Th. 22 Blacklion, cav
Fintona, tyr
Mountcharles, don
  Fr. 23 Milford, don
  Sat. 24 Derrygonnelly,
    fer
Redhills, cavan
Tydavnet, mon
  Mo. 26 Ballycastle, ant
Ballintra, don
Ballymena, ant
Buncrana, don
Clogher, tyr
Derrybeg, don
Kilcar, don
Newtownstewart, tyr
Rock, tyr
  Tu. 27 Bushmills, ant
Carrickmore, tyr
Donemana, tyr
Maghera, derry
Swanlinbar, cavan
  We. 28 Benburb tyr
Glenties, don
Kilkeel, down
Saintfield, down
Tempo, fer
  Th. 29 Antrim town
Ballyconnell, cavan
Clones, mon
Crossroads, don
Dromquin, tyr
Magherafelt, derry
Manorcunningham, don
Moville, don
  Fr. 30 Ballymena, ant
Castlederg, tyr
Killyleagh, arm
Lack, fer
Mullogh, cavan
Termonrock, tyr
Warrenpoint, down
  Sa. 31 Castledawson, der
Larne, ant
Newtownhamilton, arm
Portaferry, down

AUGUST.
  Sun. 1 Ardara, don
Clady, tyr
  Mo. 2 Altmore, tyr
Ardstrawbridge, tyr
Bailieborough, cavan
Ballybot, arm
Ballyshannon, don
Ballytrain, mon
Banbridge, down
Bangor, down
Bawnboy, cavan
Bellaghy, derry
Beragh, tyr
Callowhill, fer
Connor, ant
Crumlin, ant
Dromore, tyr
Feeny, derry
Forkhill, arm
Hollywood, down
Kilmacrenan, don
Malin, don
Monaghan town
Strabane, tyr
Tullyodonald, don
  Tu. 3 Burnfoot, don
Coleraine, derry
Dawra, cavan
Derrylin, fer
Donaghmore, tyr
Downpatrick, down
Kilcoguy, cavan
Kingscourt, cavan
Omagh, tyr
Portglenone, ant
Seaford, down
  We. 4 Aughnacloy, tyr
Belfast, ant
Castleblayney, mon
Cushendun, ant
Dungloe, don
Gortin, tyr
Killeshandra, cavan
Kesh, fer
Londonderry city
Maguiresbridge, fer
Rathfriland, down
Rosnakill, don
  Thu. 5 Armagh town
Ballinanagh, cav
Belturbet, cavan
Blownrock, don
Belcoo or Hollywell, fer
Clough, ant
Greencastle, don

Lurgan, arm
Middletown, arm
Moira, down
Muff, derry
 Fr. 6 Cross, derry
Crossmaglen, arm
Dunfanaghy, don
Draperstown, derry
Fivemiletown, tyr
Mahoolau, derry
Moy, tyr
Park, derry
Sheepbridge, down
 Sa. 7 Caradore, down
Clogher, tyr
Cookstown, tyr
Dromara, down
Dromore, down
Killincby, down
Lisnaskea, ferm
Parkgate, ant
Poyntzpass, arm
 Sun. 8 Machrecregau, tyr
 Mo. 9 Arvagh, cavan
Castlecaulfield, tyr
Castlefin, don
Castlewellan, down
Irvinestown, fer
Kerrykeel, don
Lisburn, ant
Mountnorris, arm
Newtowncrumlin, ant
Roslea, fer
Seskinore, tyr
Tubbermore, derry
 Tu. 10 Ballycastle, ant
Carnlough, ant
Cavan town
Creeslagh, don
Culdaff, don
Dungiven, derry
Enniskillen, fer
Hilltown, down
Kilnaleck, cavan
Portaferry, down
Pomeroy, tyr
 We. 11 Crossgar, down
Kilrea, derry
Shircock, cavan
Tauderagee, arm
 Th. 12 Ballybofey, den
Ballymagaurau, cavan
Carrickmacross, mon
Carrickmaquigley, don
Carrowkeel, don

Dervock, ant
Donelong, tyr
Donnelong, don
Greencastle, down
Killybegs, don
Larne, ant
Lislane, derry
Lurgan, arm
Muff, cavan
Redcastle, don
Stranorlar, don
 Fri. 13 Ballygawley, tyr
Causeway, ant
Coagh, tyr
Donegal town
Keady, arm
Letterkenny, don
 Sa. 14 Caledon, tyr
Cushendall, ant
Glen, don
Newtownards, down
Richhill, arm
Trillick, tyr
 Sun. 15 Laghey, don
Ramelton, don
 Mo. 16 Armoy, ant
Ballycarry, ant
Ballyjamesduff, cavan
Bundoran, don
Camlough, arm
Charlemont, arm
Donaghadee, down
Dunkineely, don
Dunloy, ant
Plumbridge, tyr
Stradone, cavan
Swatteragh, derry
 Tu. 17 Claudy, derry
Dundrum, down
Ederneybridge, fer
Rostrevor, down
Scotstown, mon
 We. 18 Churchhill, don
Hillsborough, down
Swanlinbar, cavan
Stewartstown, tyr
 Th. 19 Glenties, don
Ballynahinch, down
Longhgill, ant
Rathmullan, don
Sixmilecross, tyr
 Fr. 20 Ballinacarrick, don
Cootehill, cav
Cranagh, tyr
Garvagh, derry

Glasslough, mon
Markethill, arm
Pettigo, don
 Sa. 21 Ballybay, mon
Carndonagh, don
Craigbilly, ant
Killetter, tyr
Moneymore, derry
Portadown, arm
Stragowna, fer
 Mo. 23 Blacklion, cav
Carrick, don
Fintona, tyr
Milford, don
Mountcharles, don
Virginia, cavan
 Tu. 24 Ballintra, don
Churchtown, derry
Derrygonnelly, fer
Gortahook, don
Tydavnet, mon
 We. 25 Benburb, tyr
Brockagh, don
Cloghanbeg, don
Glenoe, ant
Kilkeel, down
Saintfield, down
 Th. 26 Ahoghill, ant
Antrim town
Banbridge, down
Clones, mon
Crossdoney, cavan
Crossroads, don
Drumquin, tyr
Magherafelt, derry
Manorcunningham, don
Moville, don
Port, don
 Fr. 27 Ballymena, ant
Castlederg, tyr
Donemana, tyr
Killyleagh, arm
Lack, fer
Mullogh, cavan
Raphoe, don
Termonrock, tyr
Warrenpoint, down
 Sat. 28 Ballyconnell, cavan
Castledawson, derry
Kirkcubbin, down
Newtownhamilton, arm
Tempo, fer
 Mo. 30 Ballyhays, cav
Derrybeg, don
Glenarm, ant

Newtownstewart, tyr
Rock, tyr
   Tu. 31 Ballycastle, ant
Bushmills, ant
Carrickmore, tyr
Grousehall, don
Killygordon, don
Maghera, derry

SEPTEMBER

   We. 1 Ardara, don
Aughnacloy, tyr
Belfast, ant
Broughshane, ant
Castleblayney, mon
Castlewellan, down
Gortin, tyr
Killeshandra, cavan
Kilmacrennan, don
Londonderry city
Maguiresbridge, fer
Rathfriland, down
Rossnakill, don
   Th. 2 Armagh town
Ballyjamesduff, cavan
Ballyshannon, don
Middletown, arm
Strabane, tyr
   Fr. 3 Crossmaglen, arm
Dawra, cavan
Fintown, don
Fivemiletown, tyrone
Mahoolan, derry
Moy, tyr
   Sa. 4 Ballintoy, ant
Ballynure, ant
Belturbet, cav
Clogher, tyr
Cookstown, tyr
Dungloe, don
Dromore, down
Kesh, fer
Lisnaskea, fer
Londonderry city
Poyntzpass, arm
Straid, ant
Stranorlar, don
   Mo. 6 Altmore, tyr
Ballybot, arm
Bailieborough, cavan
Ballinanagh, cav
Banbridge, down
Bawnboy, cavan
Belcoo or Hollywell, fer
Bellaghy, derry
Beragh, tyr

Blownrock, don
Dromore, tyr
Dunfanaghy, don
Kilcar, don
Kirkcubbin, down
Monaghan town
Scarva, down
   Tu. 7 Coleraine, derry
Donaghmore, tyr
Downpatrick, down
Kingscourt, cavan
Omagh, tyr
Portglenone, ant
Seaford, down
   We. 8 Buncrana, don
Crossgar, down
Irvinestown, fer
Kerrykeel, don
Kilrea, derry
Roslea, fer
Shircock, cavan
Tanderagee, arm
   Th. 9 Ballybofey, don
Larne, ant
Lurgan, arm
   Fr. 10 Ballygawley, tyr
Coagh, tyr
Creeslagh, don
Donegal town
Enniskillen, fer
Keady, arm
   Sa. 11 Caledon, tyr
Kilnaleck, cavan
Newtownards, down
Richhill, arm
   Mo. 13 Ballyshannon, don
Castlecaulfield, tyr
Glenties, don
Kells, ant
Lisburn, antrim
Mountnorris, arm
Seskinore, tyr
Tubbermore, derry
Wheathill, fer
   Tu. 14 Ballycastle, ant
Cavan town
Dungiven, derry
Glen, don
Hilltown, down
Pomeroy, tyr
Portaferry, down
Swanlinbar, cavan
Trillick, tyr
   We. 15 Hillsborough, down

Killybegs, don
Laghy, don
Ramelton, don
Stewartstown, tyr
   Th. 16 Bundoran, don
Ballynahinch, down
Dunkaneely, don
Plumbridge, tyr
Rathmullan, don
   Fr. 17 Cootehill, cav
Claudy, derry
Ederneybridge, fer
Garvagh, derry
Glasslough, mon
Markethill, arm
Scotstown, mon
   Sa. 18 Ballibay, mon
Churchhill, don
Dromara, down
Portadown, arm
Raphoe, don
   Mo. 20 Camlough, arm
Cranagh, tyr
Pettigo, don
Sixmilecross, tyr
Swateragh, derry
   Tu. 21 Dundrum, down
Killetter, tyr
Moneymore, derry
Rostrevor, down
   We. 22 Blacklion, cav
Fintona, tyr
Mountcharles, don
   Th. 23 Milford, don
Newtownards, down
Park, derry
Virginia, cavan
   Fr. 24 Arvagh, cav
Ballintra, don
Ballymena, antrim
Castlederg, tyr
Derrygonnelly, fer
Killyleagh, arm
Lack, fer
Mullagh, cavan
Tydavnet, mon
Termonrock, tyr
Warrenpoint, down
   Sa. 25 Castledawson, derry
Newtownhamilton, arm
   Mo. 27 Carrickmacross, mon
Derrybeg, don
Donemana, tyr
Newtownstewart, tyr

Rock, tyr
Tu. 28 Bushmills, ant
Carrickmore, tyr
Maghera, derry
Tempo, fer
We. 29 Ballytrain, mon
Ballyconnell, cavan
Benburb, tyr
Cushendall, ant
Forkhill, arm
Kilkeel, down
Saintfield, down
Th. 30 Antrim town
Aghygaults, don
Crossroads, don
Clones, mon
Drumquin, tyr
Magherafelt, derry
Manorcunningham, don
Moville, don

OCTOBER.

Fr. 1 Ardara, don
Ballinacarrick, don
Cross, Derry
Crossmaglen, arm
Desertmartin, derry
Draperstown, derry
Fivemiletown, tyr
Kilmacrenan, don
Mahoolan, derry
Mounthill, ant
Moy, tyr
Sa. 2 Ballinanagh, cav
Ballyshannon, don
Clogher, tyr
Cookstown, tyr
Dromore, down
Lisnaskea, fer
Poyntzpass, arm
Sun. 3 Frederickstown, tyr
Mo. 4 Altmore, tyr
Bailieborough, cavan
Ballybot, arm
Ballyhays, cav
Banbridge, down
Bawnboy, cavan
Bellaghy, derry
Beragh, tyr
Castlefin, don
Crumlin, ant
Dawra, cavan
Dromore, tyr
Dungloe, don
Kesh, fer

Kirkcubbin, down
Monaghan town
Mounthamilton, tyr
Tu. 5 Blownrock, don
Belcoo or Hollywell, fer
Coleraine, derry
Donaghmore, tyr
Downpatrick, down
Kingscourt, cavan
Lisburn, ant
Omagh, tyr
Portglenone, ant
Seaford, down
We. 6 Aughnacloy, tyr
Ballymoney, ant
Ballow, down
Belfast, ant
Castleblayney, mon
Cushendun, ant
Dunfanaghy, don
Gortin, tyr
Killeshandra, cavan
Londonderry city
Maguiresbridge, fer
Rathfriland, down
Rossnakill, don
Th. 7 Armagh town
Belturbet, cavan
Middletown, arm
Strabane, tyr
Fr. 8 Aboghill, ant
Ballygawley, tyr
Coagh, tyr
Donegal town
Irvinestown, fer
Keady, arm
Kerrykeel, don
Largymore, don
Roslea, fer
Sa. 9 Caledon, tyr
Newtownards, down
Richhill, arm
Sun. 10 Portnorris, arm
Stranorlar, don
Mo. 11 Ballyliffin, don
Belleek, fer
Castlecaulfield, tyr
Castlewellan, down
Creeslagh, don
Donaghadee, down
Enniskillen, fer
Limavady, derry
Mountnorris, arm
Seskinore, tyr
Tubbermore, derry
Tu. 12 Ballycastle, ant

Carnlough, ant
Cavan town
Cullyhanna, arm
Dungiven, derry
Hilltown, down
Killileagh, down
Pomeroy, tyr
Portaferry, down
We. 13 Crossgar, down
Kilrea, derry
Monea, fer
Shircock, cavan
Stewartstown, tyr
Swanlinbar, cavan
Tanderagee, arm
Th. 14 Ballintoy, ant
Ballybofey, don
Carrick, don
Glen, don
Larne, ant
Lurgan, arm
Trillick, tyr
Fri. 15 Clough, down
Clabby, fer
Claudy, derry
Cootehill, cav
Garvagh, derry
Glasslough, mon
Laghey, don
Markethill, arm
Ramelton, don
Sa. 16 Ballibay, mon
Bundoran, don
Dunkaneely, don
Plumbridge, tyr
Portadown, arm
Raphoe, don [gan, tyr
Sun. 17 Magheracreg-
Mo. 18 Camlough, arm
Churchhill, don
Ederneybridge, fer
Londonderry city
Scotstown, mon
Swatteragh, derry
Tu. 19 Ballynure, ant
Comber, down
Dundrum, down
Garrison, fer
Rostrevor, down
Sixmilecross, tyr
We. 20 Cranagh, tyr
Glenties, don
Gortahook, don
Hillsborough, down
Pettigo, don
Virginia, cavan

Th. 21 Ballymena, ant
Ballynahinch, down
Killetter, tyr
Moneymore, derry
Rathmullan, don
Fr. 22 Blacklion, cav
Fintona, tyr
Mountcharles, don
Sa. 23 Milford, don
Mo. 25 Ballyconnell, cavan
Ballintra, don
Derrybeg, don
Derrygonnelly, fer
Newtownstewart, tyr
Redhills, cavan
Rock, tyr
Tydavnet, mon
Tu. 26 Ballycastle, ant
Bushmills, ant
Ballyjamesduff, cavan
Carrickmore, tyr
Enniskillen, fer
Kilcar, don
Maghera, derry
Templepatrick, ant
We. 27 Benburb, tyr
Convoy, don
Dervock, ant
Donemana, tyr
Kilkeel, down
Saintfield, down
Th. 28 Antrim town
Castlereagh, down
Connor, ant
Clones, mon
Crossroads, don
Drumquin, tyr
Keady, arm
Magherafelt, derry
Manorcunningham, don
Moville, don
Tempo, fer
Fr. 29 Ballymena, ant
Castlederg, tyr
Glenarm, ant
Greyabbey, down
Killyleagh, arm
Lack, fer
Mullogh, cavan
N:towncunningham, don
Termonrock, tyr
Warrenpoint, down
Sa. 30 Castledawson, derry
Newtownhamilton, arm

NOVEMBER.
Mo. 1 Altmore, tyr
Aghygaults, don
Ardara, don
Arvagh, cavan
Bailieborough, cavan
Ballybot, arm
Ballytrain, mon
Banbridge, down
Bawnboy, cavan
Bellaghy, derry
Beragh, tyr
Carrickfergus, ant
Churchtown, derry
Crumlin, ant
Dromore, tyr
Feeny, derry
Holywood, down
Kilmacrenan, don
Kilnaleck, cavan
Maghery, arm
Malin, don
Monaghan town
Newtownsaville, tyr
Randalstown, ant
Stragowna, fer
Tu. 2 Burnfoot, don
Ballyshannon, don
Coleraine, derry
Donaghmore, tyr
Downpatrick, down
Kingscourt, cavan
Omagh, tyr
Portglenone, ant
Seaford, down
We. 3 Aughnacloy, tyr
Belfast, ant
Castleblayney, mon
Dawra, cavan
Gortin, tyr
Londonderry city
Maguiresbridge, fer
Rathfriland, down
Rossnakill, don
Th. 4 Armagh town
Ballinanagh, cav
Belturbet, cavan
Dungloe, don
Kesh, fer
Middletown, arm
Moira, down
Muff, derry
Parkgate, ant
Raphoe, don
Tullyodonald, don
Fr. 5 Blownrock, don

Belcoo or Hollywell, fer
Cross, derry
Crossmaglen, arm
Draperstown, derry
Fivemiletown, tyr
Greencastle, don
Kilcoguy, cavan
Mahoolan, derry
Moy, tyr
Port, don
Sheepbridge, down
Tanderagee, arm
Sa. 6 Ballyhays, cavan
Clogher, tyr
Cookstown, tyr
Dunfanaghy, don
Dromara, down
Dromore, down
Killinchy, down
Lisnaskea, fer
Newtowncrumlin, ant
Park, derry
Poyntzpass, arm
Stranorlar, don
Mo. 8 Ballywalter, dwn
Clough, ant
Caradore, down
Castlecaulfield, tyr
Desertmartin, derry
Irvinestown, fer
Killeshandra, cavan
Kerrykeel, don
Letterkenny, don
Lisburn, ant
Mountnorris, arm
Koslea, fer
Seskinore, tyr
Tubbermore, derry
Tu. 9 Ballycastle, ant
Carrickmacross, mon
Dungiven, derry
Hilltown, down
Portaferry, down
Pomeroy, tyr
We. 10 Culdaff, don
Creeslagh, don
Crossgar, down
Enniskillen, fer
Kilrea, derry
Shircock, cavan
Stradone, cavan
Tanderagee, arm
Th. 11 Ballybofey, don
Larne, ant
Lisbellaw, fer
Lurgan, arm

Wheathill, fer
Fr. 12 Agivey, derry
Antrim town
Armoy, ant
Augher, tyr
Ballyconnell, cavan
Ballygawley, tyr
Charlemont, arm
Coagh, tyr
Coleraine, derry
Donegal town
Keady, arm
Killybegs, don
Lislane, derry
Redcastle, don
Strabane, tyr
Sa. 13 Caledon, tyr
Carrickmaquigley, don
Castlewellan, down
Newtownards, down
Orator, tyr
Portadown, arm
Richhill, arm
Sun. 14 Derrylin, fer
Mo. 15 Ardstrawbridge, tyr
Ballycarry, ant
Bunerana, don
Cushendall, ant
Camlough, arm
Cavan town
Carrick, don
Dunloy, ant
Glen, don
Laghey, don
Ramelton, don
Swateragh, derry
Trillick, tyr
Tu. 16 Bundoran, don
Caromoney, ant
Clady, tyr
Dunkineely, don
Dundrum, down
Plumbridge, tyr
Rasharkin, ant
Rostrevor, down
We. 17 Claudy, derry
Crossdoney, cavan
Ederneybridge, fer
Hillsborough, down
Maguiresbridge, fer
Scotstown, mon
Stewartstown, tyr
Tullamore, ant
Th. 18 Ballynahinch, down

Churchhill, don
Rathmullan, don
Fr. 19 Belleek, fer
Blacklion, cavan
Cootehill, cav
Cloghanbeg, don
Garvagh, derry
Glasslough, mon
Loughgill, ant
Markethill, arm
Sixmilecross, tyr
Sa. 20 Ballibay, mon
Ballinacarrick, don
Brockagh, don
Cranagh, tyr
Portadown, arm
Pettigo, don
Mo. 22 Bangor, down
Carndonagh, don
Castlefin, don
Clough, down
Fintona, tyr
Killetter, tyr
Lurgan, arm
Moneymore, derry
Mosside, ant
Mountcharles, don
Virginia, cavan
Tu. 23 Ballyclare, ant
Ballymagauran, cavan
Milford, don
We. 24 Benburb, tyr
Ballintra, don
Donaghadee, down
Derrygonnelly, fer
Kilkeel, down
Saintfield, down
Tydavnet, mon
Th. 25 Antrim town
Clones, mon
Crossroads, don
Drumquin, tyr
Machrecregan, tyr
Magherafelt, derry
Manorcunningham, don
Moville, don
St. Johnston, don
Fr. 26 Ballymena, ant
Cloughmills, ant
Castlederg, tyr
Hamiltonsbawn, arm
Killyleagh, arm
Kirkcubbin, down
Lack, fer
Mullogh, cavan
Termonrock, tyr

Warrenpoint, down
Sa. 27 Carrowkeel, don
Castledawson, derry
Donemana, tyr
Glenties, don
Kilgolagu, cavan
Newtownhamilton, arm
Swanlinbar, cavan
Mon. 29 Ballyjames-duff, cavan
Drumadoon, ant
Derrybeg, don
Kirkcubbin, down
Newtownstewart, tyr
Rock, tyr
Tempo, fer
Tu. 30 Ballycastle, ant
Bushmills, ant
Carrickmore, tyr
Churchhill, fer
Gortahook, don
Grousehall, don
Maghera, derry
Roughfort, ant

DECEMBER

We. 1 Ardara, don
Aughnacloy, tyr
Belfast, ant
Castleblayney, mon
Cushendun, ant
Gortin, tyr
Killeshandra, cavan
Killygordon, don
Kilmacrenan, don
Larne, ant
Londonderry city
Maguiresbridge, fer
Rathfriland, down
Rossnakill, don
Th. 2 Armagh town
Ballyshannon, don
Belturbet, cavan
Middletown, arm
Strabane, tyr
Tullyodonald, don
Fr. 3 Ballyconnell, cav
Cross, derry
Crossmaglen, arm
Dawra, cavan
Draperstown, derry
Fivemiletown, tyr
Mahoolan, derry
Moy, tyr
Sa. 4 Clogher, tyr
Cookstown, tyr

Dungloe, don
Dromore, down
Kesh, fer
Lisnaskea, fer
Poyntzpass, arm
Stranorlar, don
  Mo. 6 Ahoghill, ant
Altmore, tyr
Augher, tyr
Bailieborough, cavan
Ballybot, arm
Banbridge, down
Bawnboy, cavan
Blownrock, don
Belcoo or Hollywell, fer
Bellaghy, derry
Beragh, tyr
Crumlin, ant
Dromore, tyr
Dunfanaghy, don
Kilcar, don
Kirkcubbin, down
Milltown, cavan
Monaghan town
  Tu. 7 Coleraine, derry
Donaghmore, tyr
Downpatrick, down
Kingscourt, cavan
Omagh, tyr
Portglenone, ant
Seaford, down
  We. 8 Crossgar, down
Forkhill, arm
Irvinestown, fer
Kerrykeel, don
Kilrea, derry
Roslea, fer
Shircock, cavan
Tanderagee, arm
  Th. 9 Larne, ant
Lurgan, arm
  Fr. 10 Ballygawley, tyr
Carrickmacross, mon
Clough, ant
Coagh, tyr
Creeslagh, don
Donegal town
Enniskillen, fer
Keady, arm
  Sa. 11 Caledon, tyr
Callowhill, fer
Carnlough, ant
Muff, don
Newtownards, down

Rashedog, don
Richhill, arm
Scraby, cavan
  Mo. 13 Ballyhays, cav
Camlough, arm
Castlecaulfield, tyr
Lisburn, ant
Mountnorris, arm
Portaferry, down
Seskinore, tyr
Tubbermore, derry
  Tu. 14 Ballycastle, ant
Cavan town
Dungiven, derry
Glen, cavan
Glen, don
Hilltown, down
Pomeroy, tyr
Portaferry, down
Trillick, tyr
  We. 15 Hillsborough, down
Laghey, don
Ramelton, don
Stewartstown, tyr
  Th. 16 Ballynahinch, down
Bundoran, don
Dunkaneely, don
Plumbridge, tyr
Port, don
Rathmullan, don
  Fr. 17 Cootehill, cavan
Claudy, derry
Ederneybridge, fer
Garvagh, derry
Glasslough, mon
Kilnaleck, cavan
Markethill, arm
Scotstown, mon
  Sa. 18 Ballybay, mon
Castledawson, derry
Churchhill, don
Dromara, down
Glenoe, ant
Portadown, arm
Raphoe, don
Stradone, cavan
  Sun. 19 Machrecregan, tyr
  Mo. 20 Ballybofey, don
Camlough, arm
Castlefin, don
Cranagh, tyr

Pettigo, don
Swatteragh, derry
Sixmilecross, tyr
Virginia, cavan
  Tu. 21 Ballinanagh, cavan
Castlewellan, down
Dundrum, down
Garrison, fer
Killetter, tyr
Moneymore, derry
Rostrevor, down
Stragowna, fer
Swanlinbar, cavan
  We. 22 Blacklion, cav
Cushendall, ant
Fintona, tyr
Mountcharles, don
  Th. 23 Ballytrain, mon
Ballyjamesduff, cavan
Milford, don
  Fri. 24 Arvagh, cav
Ballintra, don
Derrygonnelly, fer
Letterkenny, don
Newtownhamilton, arm
Tydavnet, mon
  Mo. 27 Armoy, ant
Derrybeg, don
Donemana, tyr
Newtownstewart, tyr
Rock, tyr
  Tu. 28 Bushmills, ant
Carrickmore, tyr
Glenties, don
Maghera, derry
Tempo, fer
  We. 29 Benburb, tyr
Kilkeel, down
Saintfield, down
  Th. 30 Antrim town
Clones, mon
Crossroads, don
Drumquin, tyr
Magherafelt, derry
Manorcunningham, don
Moville, don
  Fr. 31 Ballymena, ant
Castlederg, tyr
Killyleagh, arm
Lack, fer
Mullogh, cavan
Termonrock, tyr
Warrenpoint, down

(Corrections or alterations of Fairs should be forwarded to the Publisher before the 12th of NOVEMBER.)

STAMP DUTIES AND TAXES.

(ARRANGED ALPHABETICALLY.)

AFFIDAVIT or Statutory Declaration, made under the provisions of 5th and 6th Wm. 4th, cap. 62. .. .. 2s 6d.

AGREEMENT for Lease of any Lands, Houses, &c., or any Memorandum containing the terms and conditions on which any Lands, Houses, &c., are Let, Held, or Occupied for any term not exceeding Seven Years—Same Duty as if the Document were a Lease.

NOTE.—These Duties are denoted by Impressed Stamps.

Agreement, &c., made under hand only, and not otherwise charged or exempted from all Stamp Duty, where the matter shall be of the value of £5 or upwards, ... 0s 6d.

Agreement, &c., for Letting any Furnished Dwelling House, containing the terms or conditions on which such Houses are Let for a period less than a year, when the rent for such period shall not exceed £25, .. 2s 6d.

NOTE.—The two last Duties may be Adhesive or Impressed.

Agreements Prepared and Executed on Unstamped Paper, if brought to the Stamp Office within fourteen days from date of Execution, will be Stamped on payment of the Duty.

APPRAISEMENT or Valuation of any effects, real or personal, or of any interest therein, or of any dilapidation, or of any repairs wanted, or work done, where the amount or value shall

Not exceed £5............£0 0 3	Exceeding £40 and not £50,..£0 2 6
Exceeding 5 not ex.£10,.. 0 0 6	.. 50 .. 100,.. 0 5 0
.. 10 .. 20,.. 0 1 0	.. 100 .. 200,.. 0 10 0
.. 20 .. 30,.. 0 1 6	.. 200 .. 500,.. 0 15 0
.. 30 .. 40,.. 0 2 0	.. 500 and upwards.. 1 0 0

AWARD.—Where the Amount or Value of the Matter in Dispute shall

Not exceed £5,.......... £0 0 3	Shall ex. £100 and not £200, £0 10 0
Shall exceed 5 and not £10, 0 0 6	.. 200 .. 500, 0 15 0
.. 10 .. 20, 0 1 0	.. 500 .. 750, 1 0 0
.. 20 .. 30, 0 1 6	.. 750 .. 1,000, 1 5 0
.. 30 .. 40, 0 2 0	Exceeding £1,000 and in all
.. 40 .. 50, 0 2 6	other cases not above pro-
.. 50 .. 100, 0 5 0	vided for, ... 1 15 0

BILLS OF EXCHANGE.—Inland—Draft or Order for the Payment to the Bearer, or to Order, at any time otherwise than on demand of any sum of Money,

Not exceeding £5, .. £0 0 1	Exceed. £50 not ex. £75, .. £0 0 9
Exceed. £5 not ex.10, .. 0 0 2	.. 75 .. 100, .. 0 1 0
.. 10 .. 25, .. 0 0 3	Every £100. and fractional
.. 25 .. 50, .. 0 0 6	part of £100, ... 0 1 0

FOREIGN.—Drawn in, but payable out of, the United Kingdom.

If drawn singly or otherwise, the same Duty as an Inland Bill of the same amount and tenor.

FOREIGN Bill of Exchange, drawn (or purporting to be drawn) out of the United Kingdom, and payable within the United Kingdom.

Not exceeding £5,.. £0 0 1	Exceed. £200 not £300,... £0 3 0
Exceed. £5 not ex. 10,.. 0 0 2	.. 300 .. 400,... 0 4 0
.. 10 .. 25,.. 0 0 3	.. 400 .. 500,... 0 5 0
.. 25 .. 50,.. 0 0 6	.. 500 and upwards—
.. 50 .. 75,.. 0 0 9	Every 100 and fractional
.. 75 .. 100,.. 0 1 0	part, ... 0 1 0
.. 100 .. 200,.. 0 2 0	

NOTE.—These Duties are Adhesive.

BILL OF LADING, 6d. A Penalty of £50 is imposed for making or signing any Bill of Lading upon Unstamped Paper. A Signed Bill of Lading cannot be Stamped.

BONDS AND MORTGAGES,

Not exceeding	£25,....	£0	0	8	Not exceeding £250, ...	£0	6	3
..	50,....	0	1	3	.. 300.	0	7	6
..	100,....	0	2	6	Ex. £300, for £100 and			
..	150,....	0	3	9	fractional part, ...	0	2	6
..	200,....	0	5	0				

WARRANT—For every £100, and fractional part thereof, 6d.

CANCEL.—Adhesive Stamps for Charter Parties or Agreements must be cancelled by writing the Name and Date across the Stamp, Receipt, Draft, &c., by writing Initials and Date, or by Stamping or Impressing in Ink the Name and Date, provided that the Stamp be so obliterated that it cannot be used again.

CHARTER PARTY, 6d. A Charter Party may be Stamped after Signing, if presented within seven days after date of execution thereof by the party who first executed the same, on payment of the duty and 4s 6d penalty ; after seven days and within a calendar month, on payment of a penalty of £10, besides the duty ; and after a month it cannot be stamped. May be an Adhesive Stamp.

CONVEYANCE.—Purchase Money—

Not exceeding £5,.. ...	£0	0	6	Ex. £150 and not £175, ..	£0	17	6
Ex. £5 not ex. £10, ..	0	1	0	.. 175 .. 200, ..	1	0	0
.. 10 .. 15, ..	0	1	6	.. 200 .. 225, ..	1	2	6
.. 15 .. 20, ..	0	2	0	.. 225 .. 250, ..	1	5	0
.. 20 .. 25, ..	0	2	6	.. 250 .. 275, ..	1	7	6
.. 25 .. 50, ..	0	5	0	.. 275 .. 300, ..	1	10	0
.. 50 .. 75, ..	0	7	6	Exceeding £300, for every			
.. 75 .. 100, ..	0	10	0	£50 and fractional part			
.. 100 .. 125, ..	0	12	6	of £50, ...	0	5	0
.. 125 .. 150, ..	0	15	0				

CONTRACT NOTES, to amount or value of £5 and upwards, 1d.

COPY or Extract [certified] of any Birth or Baptism, Marriage, Death, or Burial, 1d.

COUNTY COURT FEE STAMPS.—Adhesive Stamps are now issued of the respective values of 2d, 3d, 6d, 1s, 1s 6d, 2s, 2s 6d, 5s, and 10s, which may be had at the Stamp Office, Derry.

COUNTERPART, where the Stamp Duty on first part does not exceed 5s, same Duty as on Deed. In all other cases, 5s.

DELIVERY ORDER, 1d.

DISCOUNT.—On the purchase out of stock at the Office of a Distributor or Sub-Distributor of Stamps of 1d Inland Revenue Stamps, or Impressed Bill Stamps denoting any rate of Duty not exceeding 1s: for every complete £5 worth, 2s. This discount is allowed only to licensed vendors of Stamps, no discount whatever being allowed to any other person.

DOCK WARRANT, 3d.

DRAFT or Order for the Payment of any Sum of Money to the Bearer, or to Order on demand, 1d. NOTE.—Foreign Drafts payable to bearer, or order on demand, are liable to the Duty on a Foreign Bill of like amount.

GAME LICENCE in Great Britain, or a Certificate in Ireland to Kill Game :—

If License or Certificate be taken out after April 5, and before November 1, to expire on April 5 in the following year,......	£3	0	0
To expire on October 31 in the same year in which the License or Certificate shall be taken out, ...	2	0	0
If Licence or Certificate be taken out on or after November 1, to expire on April 5 following, ...	2	0	0

A person holding a gun licence who shall, during the currency of such licence, take out a whole year's licence or certificate to kill game, may be repaid the duty on the gun licence on giving up the same to the Collector of Inland Revenue.

INCOME TAX.—Under a recent Act of Parliament, the premiums paid by a person for an Assurance on his own life, or the life of his wife, or for a Deferred Annuity to his Widow, are declared free from Income Tax, provided such Premiums do not exceed one-sixth of his returnable income.

INDENTURE of Apprenticeship in Ireland.—Where no Fee is paid, or a Fee not exceeding £10—No Duty.

LEASES, if the term is definite and does not exceed Thirty-five Years, Duties:

At a Yearly Rent, not exceeding		s.	d.			s.	d.
ing £5.	.. ..	0	6	From £25 and not exceed. £50,..		5	0
From £5 and not exceeding £10,		1	0	.. 50 ..	75,..	7	6
.. 10 ..	15,	1	6	.. 75 ..	100,..	10	0
.. 15 ..	20,	2	0	Ex. £100, and for every £50 or			
.. 20 ..	25,	2	6	fraction of £50,	.. ..	5	0

Leases exceeding Thirty-five Years.—Duties:

	Not ex. 100 years.	Ex. 100 years.
Yearly Rent not exceeding £5, ...	£0 3 0	£0 6 0
Exceeding £5 and not exceeding £10, ..	0 6 0	0 12 0
.. 10 .. 15, ..	0 9 0	0 18 0
.. 15 .. 20, ..	0 12 0	1 4 0
.. 20 .. 25, ..	0 15 0	1 10 0
.. 25 .. 50, ..	1 10 0	3 0 0
.. 50 .. 75, ..	2 5 0	4 10 0
.. 75 .. 100, ..	3 0 0	6 0 0
.. 100, for every £50 and fract. of £50,..	1 10 0	3 0 0

LEGACY DUTY on £20 and upwards—

To Children or Descendants, per cent.	£1	Great Uncle or Aunt, per cent.,	.. £6
Brother or Sister,	„ 3	Any other person,	„ .. 10
Uncle or Aunt,	„ 5		

MARRIAGE CERTIFICATE, SPECIAL, £5.

NOTICES TO QUIT must be written on a 2s 6d stamp, imposed by the 57th section of the Landlord and Tenant Act, 1870.

POWER OF ATTORNEY.—For the Sale or Acceptance of Government or Parliamentary Stock or Funds, not exceeding £20, 5s And in other cases, 10s.

PROXY, (Duty may be paid by Adhesive Stamps), 1d

PROMISSORY NOTES, (INLAND), for the payment in any other manner than to the Bearer, on demand, of any sum of money. Same Duty as on Inland Bills for like amounts

Observe.—A Promissory Note to the bearer, on demand, for a sum of money not exceeding £100, can only be lawfully issued by Licensed Bankers.

FOREIGN PROMISSORY NOTES.—Same duty as on Foreign Bills drawn out of the United Kingdom

PROBATE OF WILLS AND LETTERS OF ADMINISTRATION.—Where the Estate and Effects for or in respect of which such Probate or Letters of Administration is or are granted—

WITH WILL.								
Above the Value of	Under the Value of				Above the Value of	Under the Value of		
£20	£100	..	£0	10 0	£2,000	£3 000	..	£50 0 0
100	200	..	2	0 0	3,000	4 000	..	60 0 0
200	300	..	5	0 0	4,000	5,000	..	80 0 0
300	450	..	8	0 0	5,000	6,000	..	100 0 0
450	600	..	11	0 0	6,000	7,000	..	120 0 0
600	800	..	15	0 0	7,000	8,000	..	140 0 0
800	1,000	..	22	0 0	8,000	9,000	..	160 0 0
1,000	1,500	..	30	0 0	9,000	10,000	..	180 0 0
1,500	2,000	..	40	0 0				

In cases where the death occurred on or after 25th July, 1864, and the assets are under £100, there is no stamp duty payable. See 27 & 28 Vic., c. 56. (Same rule applies to Intestacy cases.)

WITHOUT WILL.

Above the Value of	Under the Value of		£ s d	Above the Value of	Under the Value of		£ s d
£20	£50	..	£0 10 0	£1.500	£2,000	..	£60 0 0
50	100	..	1 0 0	2 000	3,000	..	75 0 0
100	200	..	3 0 0	3,000	4.000	..	90 0 0
200	300	..	8 0 0	4,000	5,000	..	120 0 0
300	450	..	11 0 0	5 000	6,000	..	150 0 0
450	600	..	15 0 0	6.000	7,000	..	180 0 0
60)	800	..	22 0 0	7.000	8,000	..	210 0 0
8 0	1,000	..	30 0 0	8,000	9,000	..	240 0 0
1,000	1,500	..	45 0 0	9,000	10,000	..	270 0 0

PROTESTS of any Bill of Exchange or Promissory Note, where the Stamp Duty on Bill or Note does not exceed 1s—Same Duty as on Bill or Note. Protest of any other Bill or Promissory Note, or *other Notarial Act whatever*, 1s.

RECEIPT or Discharge, given for or upon the payment of Money, amounting to £2 and upwards, 1d.

SETTLEMENTS—Any instrument whereby any definite sums of money or share shall be settled upon or for the benefit of a person:

For £100 or under...............................	£0	5 0
Exceeding £100, for each £100 or part thereof	0	5 0

TRANSFER OF SHARES—In Companies 0 10 0

TRANSFER OF DEBENTURE STOCK—For every £100 or fraction thereof............................. 0 2 6

SPIRIT LICENSES.—Retailers of Spirits, whose premises are rated under £10 per annum,

(England and Ireland) . £2 4 1	At £30 and under £40..£8 16	4¾
At £10 and under £20.. 4 8 2¼	At £40 and under £50.. 9 18	5¼
At £20 and under £25.. 6 12 3¼	At £50 and upwards....11 0	6
At £25 and under £30.. 7 14 4		

ORDER as to Fees payable by Publicans to the Clerk of the Crown and Peace where those offices have been united under the "County Officers and Courts (Ireland) Act, 1877:"—

Certificate of Publican's Licence granted, ...	£0	2 6
Certificate of reversal on appeal from refusal of Justices to grant renewal of Licence.	0	2 6
Filling Notices of Publicans' Licences renewed, ...	0	2 6
On each notice of application to Quarter Sessions for any Licence for the sale of Intoxicating Liquors, whether original or by way of confirmation, renewal, or transfer, ...	0	5 0

The above fees to be denoted by *Impressed Stamps*, which may be had at the Stamp Office, Derry.

EXEMPTIONS from Stamp Duty, contained in 6 Geo. IV., chap. 41, (United Kingdom).—All Bills of Sale, Conveyances, Assignments, and other Deeds and Instruments whatever for the Sale, Transfer, or other Disposition, either Absolutely, or by way of Mortgage, or otherwise of any Ship or Vessel, or any Part, Interest, Share, or Property of or in any Ship or Vessel.

SPOILED STAMPS may be presented for allowance at the Stamp Office, Derry, within Six Months from the date of the said stamps.

Forms of Receipts, Drafts, Bills of Exchange, Agreement, and Charter Parties, if brought to the Stamp Office, will be Stamped, upon payment of the Duty.

A MILE is 5,280 feet, or 1,760 yards in length. A fathom is six feet. A league is three miles. A Sabbath Day's journey is 1,155 yards (less than two-thirds of a mile). A day's journey is thirty-two and a-half miles. A cubit is two feet. A hand (horse measure) is four inches. A palm is three inches. A span is 10½ inches. A space is three feet.

POST-OFFICE DIRECTORY.

CHIEF OFFICERS OF THE DEPARTMENT.

Postmaster-General,.......................... Lord JOHN MANNERS.
Secretary, ... JOHN TILLEY, Esq.
Secretary in Ireland, ... G. C. CORNWALL, Esq.
Secretary in Scotland, ... A. M. CUNYNGHAME, Esq.

RATES OF POSTAGE.

INLAND LETTERS.

The rates of postage to be prepaid are as follows:—

For a Letter not exceeding 1 oz.,..................					1d.
,,	exceeding 1 oz., but not exceeding 2 oz.,				1½d.
,,	,,	2 oz.,	,,	4 oz.,	2d.
,,	,,	4 oz.,	,,	6 oz.,	2½d.
,,	,,	6 oz.,	,,	8 oz.,	3d.
,,	,,	8 oz.,	,,	10 oz.,	3½d.
,,	,,	10 oz.,	,,	12 oz.,	4d.

A letter exceeding the weight of 12 oz. is liable to a postage of 1d for every ounce, beginning with the first ounce. A letter, for example, weighing between 14 and 15 ounces must be prepaid fifteen-pence.

A letter posted unpaid is chargeable on delivery with double postage; and a letter posted insufficiently prepaid is chargeable with double the deficiency. On re-directed letters the charge for re-direction is the same whether prepaid or collected on delivery.

No letter may exceed the dimensions of one foot six inches in length, nine inches in width, and six inches in depth.

NEWSPAPERS.

The following are the rates of postage on registered newspapers:—

Prepaid Rate.

On each newspaper, whether posted singly or in a packet, One Halfpenny; but a packet containing two or more registered newspapers is not chargeable with a higher rate of postage than that chargeable on a book packet of the same weight, viz., one halfpenny for every 2 oz., or fraction of 2 oz.

Unpaid Rates.

A Newspaper posted unpaid, and a packet of newspapers posted either unpaid or insufficiently paid, will be charged with the unpaid rate applicable to book packets.

The postage must be prepaid either by an adhesive stamp, or by the use of a stamped wrapper.

No newspaper can be sent through the post a second time for the original postage; for each transmission a fresh postage is required.

INLAND BOOK AND CIRCULAR POST.

A Book Packet may contain not only books, paper, or other substance in ordinary use for writing or printing, whether plain or written, or printed upon (to the exclusion of any letter, or communication of the nature of a letter); photographs, when not on glass, or in frames containing glass or any like substance; and anything usually appertaining to such articles in the way of binding and mounting, or necessary for their safe transmission by post; but also *Circulars* when they are wholly or in great part printed, engraved, or lithographed.

The rate of postage is one halfpenny for every 2 ozs. or fraction of 2 ozs.

The postage must be prepaid in full, by means of postage stamps affixed to the outside of the packet, which must be sent without covers, or in covers *entirely open at both ends, so that the contents may be easily removed for examination.* If the packet be sent without stamps it will be charged double the above rates of postage, and if not sufficiently paid it will be forwarded, charged with double the deficient postage. A book packet must not contain any letter, either sealed or open. If this rule be infringed the entire packet will be charged as a letter. If the packet be not open at the ends it will be charged at the same rate as a letter.

INLAND CARD POST.

Official Post Cards impressed, or Private Post Cards embossed, with a halfpenny stamp upon them (adhesive stamps not being accepted in payment of the postage) may be transmitted between places in the United Kingdom with letters printed or written upon back.

    The front (or stamped) side is intended for the address only, in addition to the printed words "Post Card" and "The Address only to be written on this side." There must be nothing else written, printed, or otherwise impressed on it, nor must there be any writing or printing across the stamp. On the reverse side any communication, whether of the nature of a letter or otherwise, may be written or printed. Nothing whatever may be attached; nor may the card be folded, cut, or otherwise altered. If any one of these rules be infringed, the card will be charged 1d on delivery.

    When, owing to a great and unusual influx of letters, books, &c., the transmission or delivery of the letters would be delayed if the whole mail were dealt with without distinction, Post Cards (unless paid for and posted as late letters) may be kept back until the next despatch or delivery.

    No card other than one of those issued by the Government, or a private card embossed with a halfpenny stamp at the Office of Inland Revenue, Somerset House, or at the Stamp Offices at Liverpool and Newcastle-on-Tyne, will pass under a halfpenny stamp, if it bear on it a communication of the nature of a letter.

    For information as to the conditions under which private cards are embossed with a halfpenny stamp, application must be made to the Office of Inland Revenue.

FOREIGN CARD POST.

    Post Cards intended for transmission to Foreign Countries comprised within the Postal Union are sold at the rate of 1d and 1¼d each.

PRINCIPAL COLONIAL AND FOREIGN RATES OF POSTAGE

    For Letters not exceeding half-an-ounce, to the following places:—

The entire Continent of Europe, and for Malta, Gibraltar, Cyprus, and Egypt, as well as the Dominion of Canada, Newfoundland, and the United States of America, by whatever route forwarded		0s	2½d
East Indies and Ceylon, Aden, Zanzibar, and China, *via Southampton*		0s	4d
Australia, *via Southampton*, New Zealand, via San Francisco		0s	6d
East Indies and Ceylon, Aden, Zanzibar, and China, *via Brindisi*		0s	6d
Australia, *via Brindisi*		0s	8d
Mauritius, Jamaica, British Guiana, Trinidad, and Bermuda		0s	4d
Cape of Good Hope, South African Colonies, or Ascension		0s	6d
St. Helena,		1s	0d

COLONIAL BOOK POST AND PATTERN AND SAMPLE, ETC., POST.

    To the whole of the States of Europe, Malta, Gibraltar, Cyprus, Egypt, the Dominion of Canada, Newfoundland, and the United States of America:—For printed papers and books. patterns or samples, commercial papers, ½d per 2 ozs., with the proviso that the lowest charge for a pattern or sample packet will be 1d, and that the lowest charge for a packet of commercial papers will be 2½d. The limitation of weight for a packet of commercial papers, printed papers, or books is 4 lbs., and for patterns or samples, 8 ozs. The dimensions of patterns or samples not to exceed 8 inches in length, 4 inches in breadth, and 2 inches in depth.

    To East Indies and Ceylon, Aden, Zanzibar, and China:—For commercial papers, *via Southampton*, up to 4 ozs., 2½d, and 1d for every additional 2 ozs.; *via Brindisi*, up to 4 oz., 3½d, and 2d for every 2 additional oz. For books, printed papers, and patterns, *via Southampton*, 1d; and *via Brindisi*, 2d per 2 ozs.

    To Bermuda, Falkland Islands, British Honduras, and West Coast of Africa, by any route:—For commercial papers up to 4 ozs., 2½d, and 1d for every additional 2 ozs. For books, printed papers, and patterns, 1d per 2 ozs. Limitation of weight, in all cases, 4 lbs.

    To Australian Colonies and New Zealand:—For a packet, *via Southampton*, 1d per oz. up to 2 ozs., and 4d for every additional 4 ozs.; via *Brindisi*, 2d per oz. up to 2 ozs., and 6d for every additional 4 ozs., or fraction thereof. Limitation of weight, 5 lbs., with the exception of Queensland or New South Wales, packets for which must not exceed 3 lbs. in weight.

    To Bahamas, Cape of Good Hope, Natal, St. Helena, Ascension, and Vancouver's Island:—For a packet up to 1 oz., 1d; above 1 oz. and up to 2 ozs., 2d; above 2 ozs. and up to 4 ozs., 3d; above 4 ozs. and up to 8 ozs., 6d; and so on, 3d being charged for every additional 4 ozs., the limitation of weight being 5 lbs.

PATTERNS or SAMPLES sent abroad must not be of intrinsic value.

REGISTRATION.

The British Registration Fee on every Registered Letter, Newspaper, or Book Packet posted in the United Kingdom for any British Colony or Country in the Postal Union is 2d. and the sender can obtain an acknowledgment of the delivery by paying in advance an additional fee of 2½d. For full particulars respecting Rates of Postage, Conditions of Transmission by Book or Pattern Post, &c., &c., see the "British Postal Guide," price 6d, to be obtained at the Public Office.

REGISTRATION (INLAND).

The fee for registering a letter, newspaper, book-packet, or other article, passing through the Post between any two places in the United Kingdom, is 2d.

No article addressed to initials or to a fictitious name can be registered. The prohibition, however, does not extend to articles addressed to the care of a person or firm.

Every article presented for registration must be enclosed in a strong envelope, securely fastened, and must be given to an agent of the Post-office, and a receipt obtained for it; and it should on no account be dropped into a letter-box. If, contrary to this rule, an article marked "Registered" be dropped into a letter-box, it will, *if directed to any place in the United Kingdom*, be liable to a registration fee of 8d, instead of the ordinary fee of 2d.

By law the Postmaster-General is not responsible for the safe delivery of registered articles, but henceforth he will be prepared to make good the value of a registered article lost while passing through the Post to the extent of £2 in certain cases—provided

(a) That the sender duly observed all the conditions of registration required;

(b) That the article was securely enclosed in a reasonably strong cover; and, if it contained money, that it was enclosed in one of the registered letter envelopes sold by the Post-office for the purpose;

(c) That application was made to the Secretary of the Post-office immediately the loss was discovered. (When the complaint is that the contents of a letter or packet have been abstracted, the envelope must accompany the application, otherwise the question will not be entertained.)

(d) That the Postmaster-General, whose decision shall be final, is satisfied that the loss occurred while the article was in the custody of the British Post-office, and was not caused by any fault on the part of the sender. (The word "loss" here does not include damage to an article which in fact reaches its destination, or destruction by fire or shipwreck, or by the dishonesty or negligence of any person not in the employment of the Post-office.)

No town letter-carrier is allowed to take a letter to be registered; but for the convenience of persons living in country places where no Post-office is near, letters will be registered by rural letter-carriers, who will take letters for registration on their outward and inward walks, whenever it is practicable for them to do so.

FOREIGN NEWSPAPER POSTAGE.

The following is the number of postage stamps requisite to be affixed to a copy of any registered paper not exceeding 4 oz. sent to the undermentioned countries—

Australia, *via* Southampton,	..	1d
Do., *via* Brindisi,	..	2d
Do., *via* San Francisco,	..	1d
Belgium, ...	..	1d
Brazil, ...	..	1d
British West Indies, ..	..	1d
Canada, ...	..	1d
East Indies & China, *via* Brindisi and Suez,	..	2d
Do., *via* Southampton,	..	2d
Egypt, *via* Brindisi and Suez,	..	1d
France, ...	..	1d
Germany, ...	..	1d
Gibraltar, ...	..	1d
Holland, ...	..	1d
Malta, ...	..	1d
Italy, ...	..	1d
Newfoundland, ..	..	1d
New South Wales, *via* Southampton	1d
Do., *via* Brindisi, ..	..	2d
Do., *via* San Francisco,	..	1d
New Zealand, ...	..	1d
Nova Scotia, ...	..	1d
Portugal, ...	..	1d
Turkey, ...	..	1d
United States, ..	..	1d
Van Diemen's Land, ..	..	1d
Do., *via* Brindisi and Suez, ..	2d

For Baden, Bavaria, Bremen. Frankfort, Hamburg. Hanover, Hesse, Mecklenburg, Oldenburg, Prussia, Saxony, Wurtemberg, &c.—*See Germany.*

MONEY ORDERS.

When application is made for a Money Order payable in London, or in any town where there is more than one Money Order Office, the remitter should say at which Office he wishes the Order to be paid ; otherwise it will be made payable at the Head Office. The commission, which must be paid at the time of issue, on inland money orders, is as follows :—

For sums under 10s	......	2d	For £6 and under £7	......	8d
,, 10s and under £2	......	3d	,, £7 ,, £8	......	9d
,, £2 ,, £3	......	4d	,, £8 ,, £9	......	10d
,, £3 ,, £4	......	5d	,, £9 ,, £10	......	11d
,, £4 ,, £5	......	6d	,, £10	......	12d
,, £5 ,, £6	......	7d			

An order once issued cannot be cancelled ; and should repayment or transfer to a different office be required, the remitter or payee must apply to the *paying* Postmaster according to the directions and regulations.

The scale of Commission for Orders payable abroad is as follows :—

	For Sums not exceeding			
	£2.	£5.	£7.	£10.
	s. d.	s. d.	s. d.	s. d.
If payable in France, Switzerland, Belgium, Denmark, the German Empire, Holland, Italy, Norway, Malta, Gibraltar, Constantinople, or Smyrna, - - - -	0 9	1 6	2 3	3 0
If payable in any other place abroad (including most of the Colonies) authorized to transact Money Order business with this country, - - - - - - -	1 0	2 0	3 0	4 0

No single Order can be granted for more than £10. No Money Order Business is transacted at any Post Office on Sunday, Christmas Day, or Good Friday. Every Money Order must contain the surname in full, and " the INITIAL" at least of one Christian name, both of the remitter and the payee, together with the remitter's address. In the case of Foreign Orders the full address of the payee must be given ; and if the Order be payable to a native in British India, the Tribe or Caste, and the Father's name, must also be furnished.

POST-OFFICE SAVINGS BANKS.

Post-office Savings Banks are established at all Money Order Offices in the United Kingdom, and are open for the receipt and payment of money daily during the hours appointed for Money Order business. The deposit may be one shilling, or any number of shillings, or pounds, but no fractional part of a shilling. The amount of deposits under one name must not exceed £30 in one year, nor £150, exclusive of interest, in the whole. The interest of £2 10s per cent. is allowed on every complete pound deposited, and is added to the principal on the 31st of every December. When the saving, together with the interest, amounts to £200, the interest then ceases to be allowed.

GOVERNMENT INSURANCES AND ANNUITIES.

The Act 27 and 28 Victoria, cap. 43, empowers the Postmaster-General to insure the lives of persons of either sex, between the ages of 16 and 60, for not less than £20, or more than £100. The same Act also empowers him to grant immediate or deferred annuities of not more than £50 on the lives of persons of either sex, and of the age of ten years and upwards. The persons whose lives are insured, or to whom annuities are granted by the Postmaster-General, have direct Government security for the payment of the money at the proper time. Tables of the premiums to be charged for the insurance of lives or for the grant of immediate annuities or for the grant of deferred annuities or deferred monthly allowances, without return of purchase money, or for the grant of deferred annuities or deferred monthly allowances, with return of purchase money, have been printed, and may be seen at the Post Offices which have been opened for the receipt of proposals. The premiums to be charged for the insurance of lives vary with the ages of the persons whose lives are to be insured, and with the mode in which they are to be paid.

FERMANAGH COUNTY.

Her Majesty's Lord Lieutenant of the County & Custos Rotulorum.

The Right Hon. the Earl of Erne (1840) K.P., Crom Castle, Newtownbutler; 95 Eaton Square, London, S.W.; Carlton Club, London, S.W.

High Sheriff (1878-79).

Captain Mervyn Archdale, Castle Archdale, Lisnarick.

Members of Parliament for the County.

Hon. Henry Arthur Cole (1855), (late Lieut.-Col. Fermanagh Militia, and Captain 12th Foot), Florencecourt, Enniskillen; 97 Mount-street, London, W.; Carlton Club, London, S.W.

William Humphrys Archdale, Esq., (1874), D L., J.P., Riversdale, Ballycassidy; Carlton Club, London, S.W.

Deputy-Lieutenants.

Deputy Lieutenants and Magistrates marked thus (*) have served the office of High Sheriff in this County.

Archdale, Capt. Mervyn Edward (J P. Counties Donegal and Tyrone; was M.P. for County Fermanagh, 1840-74; late Capt. 6th Dragoon Guards), Castle Archdale, Lisnarick, Trillick, Tyrone; Carlton Club, London, S.W.; Kildare-street, and Sackville-street Clubs, Dublin.

* Archdale, William Humphrys, B.A.(Oxon.), M.P. for County Fermanagh (J.P. County Tyrone), Riversdale, Ballycassidy.

Barton, Charles Robert (late Captain Fermanagh Militia), The Waterfoot, Middlebrook, Enniskillen; Mount Prospect, Kinlough, County Leitrim.

* Bloomfield, John Caldwell, Castlecaldwell, Belleek.

* Brady, John (J.P. Counties Cavan, Leitrim and Monaghan), Johnstown, Clones.

* Brien, John Dawson, Castletown, Monea, Enniskillen.

* Brooke, Sir Victor Alex., Bart., Colebrooke, Brookeborough.

Cole, Hon. John Lowry (was M.P. for Enniskillen 1859-68), Florenceconrt Enniskillen; Carlton Club, London, S.W.; Sackville-street Club, Dublin.

* Cole, Viscount (late Ens. Rifle Brigade), Florencecourt, Enniskillen; Sackville-street Club, Dublin.

* Crichton, Viscount, M.A. (Oxon.) M.P. for Enniskillen; a Lord of the Treasury (1876), Crom Castle, Newtownbutler; 95 Eaton-square, Carlton and White's Clubs, London, S.W.; Sackville-street Club, Dublin.

Enniskillen, Colonel the Right Hon. the Earl of, D.C.L., F.R.S., M.R.I.A., Fermanagh Militia (J.P. Counties Cavan and Leitrim ; was M.P. for County Fermanagh, (1831-40), Florence-court, Enniskillen ; 65 Eaton-place, Carlton and Athenæum Clubs, London, S.W. ; Sackville-street Club, Dublin.

* Irvine, Colonel John Gerard, Fermanagh Militia (J.P, County Tyrone), Killadeas, Enniskillen ; Sackville-street, Club, Dublin.

Johnstone, Samuel Yates, M.A. (T.C.D.) (called to the bar, 1839), Snowhill. Lisbellaw ; Sackville-street Club, Dublin.

Lanesborough, Right Hon. the Earl of, Lord Lieutenant and Custos Rotulorum County Cavan (1876), (Comm. R.N., Retired List), Lanesborough Lodge, Belturbet, County Cavan ; Swithland Hall, Loughborough ; Sackville-street Club, Dublin.

* Lendrum, George Cosby (J.P. Co. Tyrone) Magheracross Enniskillen.

* Madden, John (J.P. Co. Monaghan), Roslea. Manor, Clones; Kildare-street Club, Dublin.

* Montgomery, Hugh de Fellenberg (J.P. and D.L. County Tyrone), Blessingbourne, Fivemiletown, Co. Tyrone.

Richardson, Henry Mervyn, County Treasurer, Rossfad, Enniskillen.

County Court Judge and Chairman of Quarter Sessions.

Patrick Joseph Blake, Esq. (1860). Q.C., 14 Ely-place, Dublin.

Magistrates.

* Archdale, Captain Mervyn Edward, D.L. (J.P. Cos. Donegal and Tyrone) ; was M.P. for County Fermanagh, 1834-74 ; late Captain 6th Inniskilling Dragoons, Castle Archdale, Irvinestown ; Trillick. Tyrone, Carlton and White's Clubs, London, S.W. ; Kildare-street Club. Dublin.

* Archdale, William Humphrys, B.A. (Oxon.), D.L., M.P. for County Fermanagh (J P. County Tyrone), Riversdale, Bally-cassidy.

Archdall, Colonel Edward, Lieut.-Col. Fermanagh Militia (late Captain 14th Foot), Clifton Lodge, Lisnaskea ; Sackville-street Club, Dublin.

Atthill, Edward Eyre, (J.P. County Tyrone), Arvarney House, Lack.

Barton, Edward, Lieut. 27th Foot (J.P. County Donegal), Clonelly, Enniskillen ; Naval and Military Club, London, W.

* Barton, Charles Robert, D.L. (J.P. County Donegal) ; late Captain Fermanagh Militia). The Waterfoot, Pettigo ; Mount Prospect, Kinlough, County Leitrim.

Belmore, Right Hon. the Earl of, P.C., K.C.M.G., M.A. (Cantab.) (J.P. and D.L. County Tyrone ; was Under-Secretary of State, Home Department, 1856-67 ; Governor of New South Wales, 1867-72) Castleeoole, Enniskillen ; Sackville-street Club, Dublin ; Carlton Club, London, S.W.

Bloomfield, Benjamin Meynell, Castlecaldwell, Bellee ;.

* Bloomfield, John Caldwell, D.L., Castlecaldwell, Belleek.

Bloomfield, John Colpoys, Rostrevor, County Down.

Bracken, James, Toam, Blacklion.

* Brady, John, D.L.,(J.P. Cos. Cavan, Leitrim and Monaghan), Johnstown, Clones.

* Brien, John Dawson, D.L., Castletown, Monea, Enniskillen.

Brooke, Frank T., Ashbrooke, Brookeborough.

* Brooke, Sir Victor Alexander, Bart., D.L., Colebrooke, Brookeborough.

* Butler, Hon. Henry Cavandish, (J.P. and D.L. County Cavan), Innisrath, Lisnaskea ; Kildare-street Club, Dublin ; Jun. Carlton Club, London, S.W.

Cole, Hon. Arthur Edward Casamajor, Florencecourt, Enniskillen.

* Cole, Lieut.-Col. Hon. Henry Arthur, M.P. for County Fermanagh (late Fermanagh Militia, and Captain 12th Foot), Florencecourt, Enniskillen ; 97 Mount-street, London, W.; Carlton Club, London, S.W. ; Sackville-street Club, Dublin.

* Cole, Hon. John Lowry, D.L. (was M.P. for Enniskillen, 1859-68), Florencecourt, Enniskillen ; Carlton Club, London, S.W.; Sackville-street Club, Dublin.

* Cole, Viscount, D.L. (late Ens. Rifle Brigade), Florencecourt, Enniskillen ; Sackville-street Club, Dublin.

* Collum, Captain William, Bellevue, Tamlaght, Enniskillen.

Crichton, Lieut.-Col. Hon. Charles Frederick, Crom Castle, Newtownbutler.

* Crichton, Viscount, M.A. (Oxon.), D.L., M.P., for Enniskillen ; a Lord of the Treasury (1876), Crom Castle, Newtownbutler ; 95 Eaton-square, Carlton and White's Clubs, London, S.W. ; Sackville-street Club, Dublin.

D'Arcy, Major Francis (late Indian Army), Castle Irvine, Irvinestown.

Dickson, Thomas William, Bundoran, County Donegal.

Enniskillen, Colonel the Right Hon. the Earl of, D.C.L., F.R.S., M.R.I.A., D.L., Fermanagh Militia (J.P. Cos. Cavan and Leitrim ; was M.P. for County Fermanagh, 1831-40), Florencecourt, Enniskillen ; 65 Eaton-place, Carlton and Athenæum Clubs, London, S.W. ; Sackville-street Clubs, Dublin.

Evatt, Samuel Robert Bayly (J.P. and D.L., County Monaghan), Mount Lewis, Monaghan.

Gledstanes, Captain Moutray, Royal Tyrone Fusiliers (J.P. County Tyrone), Fardross, Clogher.

Gore, William, Inismore Hall, Lisbellaw.

* Graham, Francis John (J.P. County Galway), Drumgoon, Maguiresbridge ; Ballinakill Lodge, Clifden ; Union Club, London, S.W.

* Hall, Richard, 9 Norfolk-street, Park-lane, London, W.

* Hamilton-Jones, Thomas Morris (J.P. and D.L. County Armagh ; J.P. Counties Antrim, Cavan and Londonderry) Belcoo, Blacklion ; Janesborough House, Flurrybridge ; Moneyglass House, Toome ; Sackville-street Club, Dublin.

* Irvine, Colonel John Gerard, Fermanagh Militia, D.L. (J.P. County Tyrone), Killadeas, Enniskillen ; Sackville-street Club, Dublin.

Irwin, Edward, Derrygore, Enniskillen.

Johnstone, Samuel Yates, M.A. (T.C.D.), D.L., (called to the bar, 1839), Snowhill, Lisbellaw, 4 North Frederick-street, Dublin.

Lanesborough, Right Hon. the Earl of, D.L., Lord Lieutenant and Custos Rotulorum County Cavan (1876), (Comm. R.N. Retired List), Lanesborough Lodge, Belturbet ; Swithland Hall. Loughborough ; 9 Great Stanhope-street, London W.; Carlton Club, London, S.W. ; Sackville-street Club, Dublin.

Lauder, Rev. Matthew Nesbitt, A.M. (T.C.D.), (J.P. County Cavan), Gresson House, Swanlinbar.

* Lendrum, George Cosby, D.L. (J.P County Tyrone), Magheracross, Enniskillen.

Leslie, Blayney, Nutfield, Lisnaskea.

Macartney, John William Ellison (J.P. and M P., 1874. County Tyrone ; has been called to the bar in England and Ireland), The Palace, Clogher ; Kildare-street Club, Dublin ; National and St. Stephen's Clubs, London, S W.

M'Cullagh, James, jun , Esq., Pettigo.

* Madden, John, D.L. (J.P. County Monaghan), Roslea Manor, Clones ; Kildare-street Club, Dublin.

Maude, Maurice Cecly (J.P. Cos. Leitrim, Tipperary and Tyrone), Lenaghan Park, Enniskillen.

* Montgomery, Hugh De Fellenberg, D.L. (J.P. and D.L. County Tyrone), Blessingbourne. Fivemiletown.

Murray, John Scott, Mountcharles, Lisnaskea.

Nixon, Rev. Alexander Browne (J.P. County Donegal),Knockballymore, Clones.

Nixon, John (J P. County Cavan), Kilyglasson House, Blacklion, County Cavan.

Pomeroy, John Arthur, St. Angelo, Ballycassidy.

Richardson, John, Q.C. (J.P. County Monaghan), Summerhill House, Clones ; 70 Lower Baggot-street. Dublin.

* St. George, Captain Capel, ex-Paymaster Fermanagh Militia (J.P. Cos. Monaghan and Tyrone), Aughinver, Kesh ; Sackville-street Club, Dublin.

St. George, Henry Lucas (J.P. County Tyroee), Dublin.

Saunderson, Colonel Hardress Luttrell, Colonel Commanding Cavan Militia (late Captain 66th Foot). Dromard, Kesh ; Junior United Service Club, London, S.W

Scott, Richard, Scotsborough, Clones.

Smith. David (J.P. County Monaghan), Lakeview, County Monaghan.

Smyth, Edward, Enniskillen.

Stack. Ven. Charles Maurice, D.D., Tydavenet Glebe, County Monaghan.

Tipping, Gartside, Rosferry, Lisnaskea ; Sackville-street Club, Dublin.

Tottenham, Arthur Loftus (J.P. County Cavan ; J.P. and D.L. County Leitrim ; late Captain Rifle Brigade), Glenfarne Hall, Enniskillen ; Kildare street Club, Dublin ; Carlton Club. London, S.W.

Tredennick, Charles John (J.P. County Donegal), Fortwilliam, Ballyshannon.

* Tredenick, John Arnold (J.P. Cos. Donegal and Roscommon), Camlin Castle. Ballyshannon.

Walsh, Robert Pakenham, L.R.C.S.I., Enniskillen.

Winslow, Blaney Thomas, Mount Prospect, Derrylin.

Wood, John Archibald. Willoughby-place, Enniskillen.

Wrench, Frederick S. (J.P. County Monaghan). Lurganbrae, Lisnaskea ; Estate Office, Clones ; Kildare-street Club, Dublin.

County Officers.

Clerk of the Crown—Cheyne Brady, Esq. (1852).

Deputy Clerk of the Crown—William Smart, Esq., Dublin.

Clerk of the Peace—A. T. Jones, Esq. (1879), Enniskillen.

Crown Solicitor—William Henry Magrath, Esq., (1856), 9 Merrion-street. Upper. Dublin.

Sessional Crown Solicitor—John Graham, Esq., 35 Lower Ormond-quay, and Enniskillen.

Treasurer—Henry Mervyn Richardson, Esq., D L., (1858), Rossfad, Enniskillen.

Secretary to the Grand Jury—Hugh Montgomery Archdale, Esq. (1873), Drumadravey, Irvinestown.

County Surveyor—Frederick Willson, Esq., Enniskillen.

Assistant Surveyors—Messrs. John Wray, W. Crawford, J. Hoey

Sub-Sheriff—Luke Patrick Knight, Esq., P.L.G., Abbey Lodge, Maguiresbridge.

Sheriff's Returning Officer—George Knight, Esq., 14 North Great George's-street, Dublin, and Clones.

Coroners—Blayney Leslie, Esq., J.P., Nutfield, Lisnaskea; William Gilbert, Esq., Clonee, Ederney.

BARONY CESS COLECTORS.

Clanawley—James Willis, Moneen, Florencecourt.
Clankelly—James West, Kilgarrow, Newtownbutler.
Coole—Robert Clendinning, Newtownbutler.
Knockninny—A. Johnston, Drumsheemuck, Derrylin.
Lurg—Charles Richardson, Rossfad, Ballycassidy.
Magheraboy—John Kerr, Coagh, Enniskillen.
Megherastaphena—James Forster, Drumbrughas, Lisnaskea.
Tyrkennedy—William Muldoon. Enniskillen.

COUNTY FERMANAGH.

FERMANAGH is an inland county of Ulster, bordering on the Counties Tyrone, Monaghan, Cavan, Leitrim, and Donegal. Its greatest length is 45 miles and its breath 29. Its area comprises 457, 95 acres, of which 106,530 are under tillage; 243,251 in pasture; 5,909 in plantations; 55,248 of waste bog and mountains; 210 of towns; and 46,431 of water. The county is bisected by the waters of Lough Erne in a north-west direction, or a little transversely. The south-west, by the River Arney, which flows from Lough Macnean, is a due easterly direction to Lough Erne.

The trade of the county is generally concentrated in Enniskillen, and as reference is made to it in our notes thereon, it is needless to go into any detail here. Yet as the personal statistics might be interesting, we will make a short remark thereon, and in doing so, shall confine ourselves to a review of certain trades between the years 1841 and 1871, that have very much decreased. For instance, in 1841 we had 4,720 spinners of flax; 269 spinners of wool; while spinners of unspecified classes amounted to 16,607. Of weavers of linen there were 354; while unspecified classes of weavers were given as 1,289. Comparing these figures with the last return given in the Census for 1871, we find a sad decrease. In fact the many trades and occupations then followed, when compared with those now carried on, show that a great decrease has taken place; but this may be on account of the decrease in the population. The facilities for communication are, however, very much improved since 1841. There is now direct railway communication by the Great Northern Line from Dublin to Derry, and recently the Sligo, Leitrim and Northern Counties Railway has been opened for traffic from Enniskillen to Belcoo, and is likely to prove, when complete as far as Sligo, a very useful line. The educational statistics show a decided increase, for instance in 1841 there were 26,386 males over 5 years who could not read or write, while 36,196 represented the number of females. In the year 1871 the number of males were 15,544, and females 17,674. The county sends 2 members to Parliament, the present representatives being William H. Archdale, Esq., M.P., Riversdale; and the Hon. H. A. Cole, Florencecourt. The population in 1871 was 92,794, or 18,957 families.

Fermanagh was constituted a county in the Eleventh year of Elizabeth, and was not reduced to order at "The Plantation of Ulster," in the reign of James I. The forfeitures consequent on the Rebellion in 1641, altered very much the social phases of the county, and considerably increased the possessions of the English

and Scotch settlers. The historical events of any note occurred
at the epochs of that Rebellion and of the war of the Revolution,
and are referred to at a great length by the writer of the work
" Tully Castle." In 1703, John Verney, the descendent of an old
family long settled in Buckinghamshire, was created Baron Verney
of Belturbet and Viscount Fermanagh. The title is now extinct.

LOUGH ERNE

A FINE river, and two large magnificent lakes, the former chiefly,
and the latter almost wholly in County Fermanagh· The river
issues from Lough Ganny or Gawna, on the mutual border of
the Counties of Longford and Cavan ; and runs north-west
through the latter county, beautifying much of it with locustrine
expansions and sylvan and meadowy meanderings, and receiving
in its progress the tribute of the Cootehill and Woodford rivers,
and of various minor streames. From the foot of Lower Lake
Erne to Donegal Bay, it has a westerly run of 2½ miles in County
Fermanagh, and 5½ miles across the extremity of the southern
wing of County Donegal ; and it sweeps athwart a considerable
amount of fine scenery and makes a fine rapid at Belleek, a
splendid cataract at Ballyshannon, and two or three intermediate
accelerations of current. Upper Lough Erne, the middle or
connecting reach of the River Erne, and Lower Lough Erne
unitedly extend north-east westward, from end to end of County
Fermanagh, and very nearly along its middle, so as to cleave it
into two almost equal longitudal sections by a vast and very
varied aqueous basin. Swells, undlaions, diversified slopes, and
isolated limestone hills, form the greatest part of both the margin
and the sky-line of the grand valley ; but, on the other hand, low
marshy, and meadowy flats, broadly fringe a considerable portion
of both the upper and connecting reach of the river, and the
Poola Fookn range of table-land, rising to an altitude of above
1,000 feet, flanks a very large proportion of the Lower Lough.
" Lough Erne, round its whole circumference, says Mr. Ingles,
" does not offer one tame and uninteresting view ; every where
there is beauty, and beauty of a very high order. In some places
the banks are thickly wooded to the water's edge. In other places,
the fairest and smoothest slopes rise from the margain, shaping
themselves into knolls and green velvety lawns ; here and there
finely wooded promontories extend far into the lake. forming calm,
sequestered inlets and bays ; and sometimes a bold foreground,
not perhaps of mountains. but of lofty hills, juts forth, and con-

trasts finely with the richness and cultivation on either side. And what shall I say of the numerous islands, far more numerous than those on Windermere, and as beautiful as the most beautiful of them; some of them densely covered with wood, some green and swelling, and some large enough to exhibit the richest union of wood and lawn; some laid out as pleasure ground, with pleasure houses for those to whom they pertain; and some containing the picturesque ruins of ancient and beautiful edifices. Nor must I forget the magnificient mansions that adorn the banks of Lough Erne, and which add greatly to the general effect of the landscape. I shall not easily forget, nor would I ever wish to forget, the the delightful hours I one day spent on the shores of this more than Winderemere of Ireland. It was a day of uncommon beauty; the islands seemed to be floating on a crystal sea; the wooded promontories threw their broad shadows half across the still bays; the fair slopes and lawny knolls stood greenly out from amongst the dark sylvan scenery that intervened; here and there a little boat rested on the bosom of some quiet cove; and in some of the shallow bays. or below the slopes of some of the green islands, cattle stood single or in groups in the water. I confidently assert that Lower Lake Erne, take it all in all, is the most beautiful lake in the Three Kingdoms, and but for the majestic Alpine outline that bounds the horizen on the upper part of Lake Leman, Lake Leman itself could not contend in beauty with this little-visited lake in the County of Fermanagh."

The Upper Lake measures $8\frac{1}{2}$ miles in extreme length, by $3\frac{1}{4}$ in extreme breath; and the Lower Lake $12\frac{1}{2}$ by $5\frac{1}{2}$.

Abraham Creighton, Esq., only son of David Creighton, who gallantly defended his family seat of Crom Castle, against the Jacobite forces in 1689, was created Baron Erne of Crom Castle, in 1768, and John. the second Baron, was successively in 1781 and 1789, created Viscount Creighton and the Earl of Erre, and the present Earl of Erne has received the additional title of Baron of Fermanagh and Knight of St. Patrick.

DEVENISH ISLAND

SITUATE about $2\frac{1}{2}$ miles from Enniskillen by water, in a north-west direction, contains about 80 Irish acres, and the soil is exceedingly fertile. Upon it stands one of the most perfect round towers in Ireland, and the old Abbey of Devenish. The edifices that were, and the other antiquities on the island. are all usually associated in a Monastic way, with the name of St. Molaisse, or Mulush, who died in 563. According to Usher and Ware, however, it is said that the alleged Monastery of St. Molaisse was originally a Culdean establishment, where the disciples of St. Columba exercised their piety. In the Ulster Annals it is said, that in the year 1130 was formed the Abbey of Daminis, now Devenish. Ware, however, supposes this to refer to the repairing of the ancient establishment. The description of the Abbey-Church, the Church of St. Molush, and the building called St. Molush's house, given in the Parliamentary Gazetter of 1841, when compared with the present appearance of the ruins, shows that the hand of time has dealt rather severely with them. At that time St. Molush's house stood 30 feet long and 18 feet wide, and was entirely roofed and finished with cut stone, nothing now remains, however, save about 3 feet high of the walls. The Tower stands 82 feet high by 49 feet in circumferanee. The name Devenish is a corruption of *Damh Inis* "the Ox's Island." Devenish gives the name to the parish of Devenish, a large parish in Fermanagh. Recently the ruins were conserved by the Board of Public Works, when many interesting pieces of stone work were brought to light, including a large Celtic Cross which contains some beautiful tracery, and which is now firmly erected near the Abbey. To the Enniskillen Board of Guardians, belongs the credit of having recently had substantial walls built round each graveyard, and by this means has stopped the unseemly sight that tourists and visitors were obliged to gaze on with pain, that is—the trampling of cattle over the graves of the dead.

ENNISKILLEN.

ENNISKILLEN the capital of Fermanagh, is situate in the baronies of Tyrkennedy and Magheraboy. The principal portion of the town is built on an island which divides Upper and Lower Lake Erne. At the time of the Plantation of Ulster, James I, granted the town to William Cole, Esq., and his heirs for ever, for the purpose amongst others of planting it with English and Scotch settlers. In the Rebellion of 1841, the town was ably defended against the Irish Army by its founder, who was then Sir William Cole. It also played a prominent part in the wars of 1689 and 1690. The corporation which existed under the grant of James, by the title of "Portrieve Free Burgesses and Commonalty of Enniskillen," of whom Sir William Cole was the first provost, became dissolved by Act of Parliament, and the property vested in Town Commissioners, who became incorporated under the Act of 9th of George IV. It was also constituted a Parliamentary Borough under the original grant, and still continues to send a member to Parliament, the present representative is Viscount Crichton, M.P., one of the Lords of the Treasury. The town during the last twenty years has been considerably improved, both in its appearance and sanitary condition by its Town Commissioners, and the arrangements as to water supply, cleansing the town, &c., are at present superior to those of any provincial town in the north of Ireland, and reflect the greatest possible credit on the Commissioners and their Officers. Considerable additions have also been made to the number of buildings, dwelling-houses, &c., particularily in the direction of the Markets, and in Paget and Eden street, which have been almost altogether rebuilt by the Earl of Enniskillen. The late Mr. John Collum also aided very considerably in the improvement of the town. The town at once strikes a stranger by the peculiarity of its position, and beauty of its surroundings. You enter it by a bridge, and after passing through its principal thoroughfare, you may take your departure by passing over another bridge, distant from the former about an English mile. The town is distant from Dublin, by rail, 120 miles, and is one of the principal stations on the Great Northern Line, between Dublin and Derry. A new line, the Sligo, Leitrim, and Northern Counties Railway, has recently been opened for traffic, from the terminus at Enniskillen as far as Belcoo, when complete it will connect Enniskillen with Sligo, and will be of great advantage to the developement of trade. The population in 1871, was 5,836, inhabiting 943 houses. Two newspapers are in town, the THE FERMANAGH MAIL, published every Monday and Thursday, is a highly respectable and widely circulated paper, and a desirable medium for advertising; and the THE IMPARTIAL REPORTER, which is published every Thursday, The public buildings are the Episcopalian Church, Roman Catholic Church, Presbyterian and Methodist Meeting Houses, Courthouse, Prison, Infirmary, Town and Protestant Halls, Portora Royal, the Nationals (Abbey and Mary St.), Model, Convent, Christian, Brothers' and Erasmus Smyth's Schools; the Provincial, Ulster, Belfast, Hibernian, and Savings Banks; the Brewery, Spool Mill, Union Workhouse, 3 Military and 2 Constabulary Barracks. The spacious room on the ground floor of the Townhall was opened on Thursday, 6th November last, as a Public Reading Room, and is supplied with the leading daily and weekly papers, periodicals, &c., affording every comfort and facility for self-improvement. The portion now standing of the ancient Castle of Enniskillen, forms part of one of the Military Barracks. It is a very ancient structure, and is mentioned in the Annals of the Four Masters as having been given up, in 1459, to Donnall Ballagh Maguire, one of the ancient Lords of Fermanagh.

SCHOOLS.

Portora Royal School.

THIS School, together with similar institutions in the Counties Tyrone, Armagh and Donegal, were founded in the reign of King James I., in connection with the Settlement of Ulster. The School is beautifully and healthfully situated on the brow of a hill, overlooking Lough Erne, and commanding a most magnificent view of the picturesque scenery which, wherever you turn, meets the eye. It is one of the most richly endowed of all our Irish public schools, and has also surpassed them all in collegiate and academic distinctions.

There are TWENTY-THREE EXHIBITIONS attached to the School, viz., Five of £25, and Five of £15, tenable by Boys in the School, and Five of £40, and Five of £30, also Three of £7, tenable by pupils of the School who have entered Trinity College, Dublin. There are also Eight Prizes, viz., Four of £10, and Four of £5, offered each year for proficiency in English subjects; also " The Frederick Steel Memorial Prize " of £12 for Latin and Greek Composition.

Head Master—Rev. William Steel, D.D.

The Model School.

NEXT to Portora Royal School, the most important educational establishment in the town, is the District Model School, in which nearly three hundred children receive the benefit of a thoroughly sound English, mathematical and scientific education. The building is of brick on a limestone basement, and, though not pretending to much architectural beauty, is internally fitted up with all appliances, in the shape of maps, diagrams and apparatus, to satisfy every modern educational want.

The institution consists of three departments: Boys', Girls', and Infants', and is conducted strictly in accordance with the principles of Irish national education, namely, to afford combined literary and moral, and separate religious instruction to children of all persuasions, and so that no attempt shall be made to interfere with the peculiar religious tenets of any description of Christian pupils. The teaching staff in the Boys' School consists of the Head Master, Mr. Charles Morris, two assistants, Messrs. Moore and Stokes, eight resident pupil Teachers, and two paid monitors. The Girls' school is conducted by Miss Greaves, Head Mistress, Miss Maher, assistant, and five monitresses. The principal of the Infants' department is Miss Tully, who is assisted by Miss Harpur, and three monitresses. It will be thus seen that there is a very large staff of teachers. The school is not only an educational, but also a training instituation, as many as eighty young teachers having been educated for their profession, since the opening of the establishment in 1867.

During the winter months, scientific lectures in connection with the Department of Science and Art, are delivered by the Head Master.

The pupils are annually examined about Christmas by the Head Inspector of the province, James Morell, Esq., and by the District Inspector and Manager of the Schools, James J. Hynes, Esq.

The other Schools

Are the Christian Brothers', East Bridge street; the Erasmus Symth's Schools, Forthill; and the National Schools in Abbey and Mary Street; the Misses Bayly's excellent Private School in Darling street, and a similar School kept by the Miss Dwyers in the Manse, Wesley street.

LOCAL DIRECTORY.

Henry Plews, Esq., Prospect House, Tonystick, Enniskillen, the Traffic Manager, of the north-west district of the Great Northern Railway of Ireland.

James Plews, Esq., Willoughby place, General Manager for the Sligo, Leitrim and Northern Counties Railway.

HOUSES OF PUBLIC WORSHIP.

Church of Ireland, Church street— Rev Samuel Greer, M.A.. T.C D., Curates — Rev. Thomas Hughes, LL.D., and Rev. D. O'Leary, B.A. Service at 12 o'clock, noon, and 6 o'clock, p.m. There is a service for the Troops at 9 a.m. Chaplain, Rev. David O'Leary, B.A.

Roman Catholic, Darling street—
Very Rev. James M'Meel, P.P,
D.D. Curates—Rev. Felix Hacket,
Rev. E. M'Kenna, and Rev. B.
Boylan. Services at 9, 12 & 6.
Presbyterian Church, East Bridge st.
—Rev. Alex. C. Maclatchy, M.A.
Services at 12 noon and 6 p.m.
Wesleyan Methodist, Darling street
—Rev. John Dwyer and Rev. Wm.
Harper. Rev. John Ker, General
Missionary for District. Services,
12 noon and 7 p.m.

MASONIC.

There are three Masonic Lodges,
and two Royal Arch Chapters, that
hold their meetings in the Townhall.

POST OFFICE.

G. J. Benson, Esq., Postmaster.
Outgoing Mails—
For Tempo, Lisbellaw, Tamlaght,
Churchhill, Derrygonnelly, &c.,
Letters can be posted up to 5.55
a m.
For Florencecourt, Manorhamilton,
Letterbreen and Blacklion, Letters
can be posted up to 7.5 a.m.
For Derry, Omagh, Belfast, Scotland,
Letters can be posted up to 7.5 a.m.
Letters can be registered for the above
bags until 8 o'clock the previous
evening.
For Derry, Omagh, Strabane, Belfast
and Scotland, Letters can be posted
until 10.45 a.m., with extra 1d.
stamp up to 10.50 a m., and can be
registered up to 10.15 a.m.
For Dublin Mail, England, Scotland,
Dundalk, Clones, Lisnaskea, Derry,
Omagh, Belfast, Ballyshannon and
Bundoran, Letters can be posted
until 12.40 p.m., with extra stamp
up to 12.50 p.m., and be registered
up to 12.10 p.m.
For Sligo, Manorhamilton, Glenfarne,
Blacklion and Florencecourt, Letters can be posted until 1 30 p.m.,
with an extra stamp up to 1.40 p.m.,
and can be registered up to 1.0 p m.
For Dublin Night Mail, England,
Scotland, Belfast, Derry & Omagh,
Letters can be posted until 6.55 p.m.

with extra stamp up to 7.15 p.m.,
and can be registered up to 6.25 p.m.
Incoming Mails—
From England, Scotland, Dublin,
Belfast, Derry, Strabane & Omagh
delivered at 7.0 a.m.
From Dublin (day mail), England,
Scotland, Belfast, Derry, Omagh,
Strabane, Sligo, Manorhamilton,
Blacklion, Florencecourt, Bun-
doran, Ballyshannon, Belleek,
Irvinestown, &c., delivered at 2 p.m.
Omagh, Blacklion, Manorhamilton,
Florencecourt, Churchhill, Derry-
gonnelly, Lisbellaw. Tempo, &c.,
delivered at 7.30 p.m.
Money Order, Savings Bank, and
Government Insurance and Annuity
Business Transacted, on Week
Days from 9 a.m., till 6 p.m. and on
Saturdays till 8 p.m. No business of
this description transacted on Sun-
day, Good Friday, or Christmas Day.
Telegraph Business is transacted
from 8 a.m. to 8 p.m. on Week Days,
and on Sundays from 9 a.m. to 10
a.m. and from 3 p.m. till 4 p.m.
The Office is open on week days
from 7 a.m. to 8 p.m., and on Sunday from 7 a.m. to 10 a.m., but
letters for despatch the same evening
can be posted up to 6.55 p.m.

SOLICITORS.

Joseph Alexander, Townhall street.
J. Whiteside Dane. East Bridge st.
John Graham, Local Crown Solicitor,
Darling street.
Robert Keys, Fort Lodge.
John C. Macniffe, Church street.

*Commissioners for taking Acknow-
ledgements to Deeds by Married
Women.*
John Graham, solicitor, Darling st.
Henry N. Lowe, High street.
William Muldoon, East Bridge st.

*Commissioners for taking Affida-
vits for the Supreme Courts of Judi-
cature in Ireland.*
H N. Lowe, High street.
Wm. Muldoon, East Bridge street.
O. Ternan, Townhall street.

SURGEONS, PHYSICIANS, APOTHE- CARIES AND CHEMISTS.

Edward Bagot, L.R C.S.I. & L Q.C.P.I., Carlton House, Darling street.
Thomas Vesey Bell, L.R.C P I., L.M., L R.C.S.I., Church street.
William Bell, Church street.
Dr. Cullen, Church street.
Baptist Gamble, L.R.C.S I., Darling st.
John Gunning, jun., L.R.C.S I, Darling street.
John Gunning & Sons, Darling st.
Obadiah Ternan, L.A. & L.M , Town-hall street.
Robert P. Walsh, L.R.C S.I., and L Q.C P.I.. Surgeon-Major Fermanagh Militia, Darling street.

BANKS.

Belfast, Townhall st.—W. Williams. Esq., Manager.
Hibernian, Darling street—Charles R. Hearne, Esq., Manager.
Provincial, Church street — George Stewart, Esq., Manager.
Uster, Darling st.—Samuel Clarke, Esq., Manager.
Savings Bank, Church street—Chas. J. C. Jones, Esq., Actuary.

ARCHITECT.

Thomas Elliott, Esq., Darling street.

LAND SURVEYORS.

Robert Boyle, Wellington Place.
Joseph Weaver, 5 Anne street.
John Wray, C.E , High street.

AUCTIONEERS.

W. A. Ferguson, Wellington Place,
John Gillin, Queen street.
G. Irvine, Darling street

PHOTOGRAPHR.

G. F. Crowder.

PROFESSORS OF MUSIC.

M. Arnold, Church Organist, Darling street.
J. Loretto, Coleshill Terrace.

INSURANCE AGENTS.

Joseph Alexander, Solicitor, Townhall street.
George Darragh, Church street.
John Graham, Solicitor, Darling st.
Andrew Law, Watchmaker, High st.

INSURANCE AGENTS.—(continued.)

J. Lunham, Acount., Provincial Bank
John Lemon, East Bridge street.
Henry N. Lowe, Printer, 7 High st.
Y. Pratt, Accountant, Ulster Bank.
G. Stewart, Manager Provincial Bank
W. Williams, Manager, Belfast Bank.
Whitley Brothers, High street.

NEWS AGENTS.

James Kenny, High street
Joseph Weaver, Anne street.
Geo. B. White, Townhall street
Johnny M'Caffrey, Eden street.

VETERINARY SURGEON.

Wm. White, East Bridge street.

CIVIL ENGINEER.

John Wray, Town Surveyor.

Trades' Directory.

AGRICULTURAL IMPLEMENT AGENTS.

Bradshaw & Co., East Bridge street.
T. Gordon, Church street.
J. Lemon, East Bridge street.

ÆRATED WATER MANUFACTURER.

W. Cooney, High street.

BAKERS.

T. Cox, Belmore street.
W. Colhoun, Darling street.
W. Coalter, High street.
J. Coalter, Church street.
G Darragh, Church street.
M. Frith, Belmore street.
T. Hughes, Darling street.
H. Hughes, Townhall street.
R. Hamilton, East Bridge street.
T. Johnston & Co., High street.
J. Mayers, Church street.
W. B. Morrison, Darling street.
T. Murphy, East Bridge street.
J. M'Bride, Darling street.
Whitley Brothers, High street.

BARBER.

J. Goddard, Diamond.

BELLHANGERS.

See Plumbers and Gasfitters.

BOOKSELLERS AND STATIONERS.

Mrs. M. Elliott, East Bridge street.
W. & J. Gibson, East Bridge street.
J. Irvine, East Bridge street.
H. N. Lowe, High street.
W. Trimble, East Bridge street.
Geo. B. White, Townhall street.
J. Weaver, Darling street.

BOOT AND SHOE SHOPS.

Burgess Bros , Middleton street.
R. & J. Dick, & Co., Townhall street.
W. Irvine, Darling street.
H. N. Lowe, High street.
T. M'Keague, Townhall street.
J. Noble, East Bridge street.
J. Verner, High street.

BOOT AND SHOE MAKERS.

J. Brennan, Queen street.
W. Irvine. Darling street.
J. Love, Paget street.
M'Cauley Bros , Wellington Place.
B. M'Cusker, High street.
T. M'Keague, Townhall street.
C. Maguire, Brooke street.
J. Noble, East Bridge street.

BREWERS.

Messrs. Downes, Anne street.

BUILDERS AND CARPENTERS.

W. Campbell, East Bridge street.
A. Crozier, Darling street.
J. Elliott, Wellington Place.
D. Gresham, Darling street.
J. Harvey, Belmore street.

BUTCHERS.

J. Blakely, Darling street.
E. Blakely, Water street.
P. Crumley, Townhall street.
D. Donnelly, High street.
B. Scollan, Water street.

BUTTER MERCHANTS.

J. Clegg. Brooke street.
Gillespie & Co., the Brooke.
Cooper & Co., Diamond.
E. M'Nulty, High street.

CABINETMAKER.

H Wallace, Eden street.
J. Mulhern, Market street.

CARTWRIGHTS.

R. Gregg, Paget street.
T. Orr, Gas Court.

CHINA, DELPH & GLASS MERCHANTS.

J. Gordon, Church street.
J. Johnston, High street.

CLOCK & WATCHMAKERS.

P. Clancy, Townhall street.
A. Law, High street.
J. Molyneux, High street.
R. J Richards, Townhall street.
P. Sullivan The Brooke, (Agent for
　　Langdon & Co., Birmingham.)

COACHBUILDERS.

S. Beatty, Brooke street.
D. Maguire, Forthill street.
E. Maguire, Brooke street.
M. M'Keown, Darling street.
P. Shannon. Wellington Place.

COAL MERCHANTS.

Bradshaw & Co.. East Bridge street.
D. Gresham, Darling street.
J. Lemon, East Bridge street.

CONFECTIONERS.

T. Cox, Belmore street.
M. Frith & Co., Belmore street.
R. Hamilton, East Bridge street.
W. B. Morrison, Darling street.
T. Murphy, East Bridge street.
J. M'Bride, Darling street.

COOPERS.

Francis Creegan, Market street.
Thomas Maxwell, Market street.
Patrick Reilly, Market street.

DRUGGISTS.

W. Bell, Church street.
J. Gunning & Sons, Darling street.
O. Ternan, Townhall street.

DRAPERS AND HABERDASHERS.

W. R. Cooney, High street.
J. Dundas & Co., Darling street.
J. T. Dundas, Darling street.
J Johnston, High street.
J. Kenny & Co., High street.
P. & J. Maguire, Church street.
J. Maguire & Co., Church street.
Owen M'Brien, Church street.
M. M'Donnell, East Bridge, street.

DRAPERS & HABERDASHERS.—
(Continued.)

J. & H. Roberts, Diamond House.
W. Robinson, High street.
W. Teele, Townhall street.
T. A. Wylie, High street.
J. Wray, High street.

DRESSMAKERS.

The Misses Blair, Belmore street.
The Misses Brady, Wesley street.
The Misses Carlton, Townhall street.
The Misses Chittick, New Row.
The Misses Curren, Belmore street.
W. R. Cooney, High street.
Miss Henderson, Darling street.
J. Johnston, High street.
Miss Latimer, Darling street.
Miss Morrison, Forthill street.
Mrs. Oats, Castle street.
Miss Wilson, East Bridge street.
T. A. Wyley, High street.
W. Teele, Townhall street.

EGG MERCHANTS.

J. Clegg, Brooke street.
J. Cooper, The Diamond.
Francis Doherty, Henry street.
J. C. Gillespie, Brooke street.
J. M'Grory, Henry street.
E. M'Nulty, High street.
A. Wilson, Brooke street.

GROCERS.

Burgess Bros., Middleton street.
G. Black, Church street,
A. Cassidy, High street.
J. Coalter, Church street.
Wm. Coalter, High street.
J. Cleland, Darling street.
T. Cox, Belmore street.
T. Crowe, High street.
W. Colhoun, Darling street.
G. Darragh, Church street.
A. Frith, Townhall street.
T. Gordon, Church street.
E. Gamble, Anne street.
B A. Graham, Darling street.
W. E. Gordon, Townhall street.
J. Gillin, Queen street.
J. Haren, Darling street.
J. Jordan, High street.
T. Johnston & Co., High street.
J. Law, High street.
A. Law, High Street.

GROCERS.—(Continued.)

H. R. Lindsay Townhall street.
J. Latimer, Middleton street.
J. Mayers, Church street.
J. Mitchell, Forthill street.
T. Murphy, East Bridge street.
J. M'Bride, Darling street.
J. M'Elgunn, Anne street.
E. M'Nulty, High street.
M O'Brien, East Bridge street.
T. Plunkett, High street.
J. Quinton, Church street.
J. Verner, High street.
G. Wadsworth. Brooke street.
Whitley, Bros., High street.
J. & T. Wilson, East Bridge street.

GUNSMITHS.

T. Irwin, East Bridge street
R. Smith, East Bridge street.

HARDWARE MERCHANTS.

W. Boyd, High street.
Bradshaw & Co, East Bridge street.
T. Gordon, Church street.
W. E. Gordon, Townhall street.
J. Law, High street.
A Law. High street
J. Lemon, East Bridge street.

HATTER.

J. Murray, East Bridge street.

HORSESHOERS AND BLACKSMITHS.

M. Boland, Brooke street
J. Drum, Paget street.
J. Keown, Cross street.
W. White, East Bridge street.

HIDE MERCHANTS.

F. Little, Market street.
W. Lowry, Belmore street.

HOTELS.

Imperial, Townhall street, G. Willis,
Railway, Forthill st., P. M'Namee.
Royal, East Bridge st., E. Monaghan
White Hart, Townhall street, the
    Misses Willis.

LEATHER MERCHANTS.

Burgess Bros., Middleton street.
B. A. Graham, Darling street.
J. Verner. High street.
Whitley, Brothers, High street.

NEW AND SECOND-HAND CLOTHES DEALERS.

Thos, Brannan, Townhall street.
Patrick Brady, East Bridge street.
John Campbell, Townhall street.
Matthew Campbell, East Bridge st.
James Carroll, East Bridge street.
John Cox, Townhall street.
Patrick Gordon, Water street.

PAINTERS, GLAZIERS AND PAPER HANGERS.

C. Blakely, Mary street.
Daniel Gonigle, Queen street
B. Hughes, East Bridge street.
D. Maguire, Market street.
D. M'Kenna, Townhall street.
J. M'Gorty, Forthill street.
T Nelson, New Row.
C. Nelson, New Row.

PAWNBROKERS

T. Brannan, Townhall street.
M. M'Donnell, East Bridge street.

PLUMBERS AND GASFITTERS.

D. Gresham, Darling street.
J. Lemon, East Bridge street,
J. Tickle, Belmore street.

POULTERERS.

W. Gillan, Queen street.
J. Rafferty, Henry street

PRINTERS.

W. & J Gibson, East Bridge street.
H. N. Lowe, High street.
T. R. J. Polson, Wellington Place.
William Trimble, East Bridge street

PROVISION CURERS.

Cooper & Co., The Diamond.
J. Donnelly, High street.
J. Jordan, High street.
F. Little, Water street.
J. M'Elgunn, Anne street.
T. Plunkett, High street.

ROOM PAPER WAREHOUSES.

T. Gordon, Church street.
B. Hughes, East Bridge street.
J Molyneux. High street.
M. E. & E Parkinson, Townhall st.

SALT MERCHANTS.

Bradshaw & Co., East Bridge street.
W. Coalter, High street.
J. Lemon, East Bridge street.

SADDLERS

M. Clarke, Belmore-street.
A. Johnston, Market street.
J. Maguire, Market street.
R M'Clean, Townhall street.
P. M'Mullan, Henry street.
J. Monaghan, Townhall street.

SPIRIT AND WINE MERCHANTS.

G. Black, Church street.
J. Campbell, Forthill street.
J. Carson, Darling street.
T. Corrigan, Church street.
W. Cooney, High street.
A. Creden, Queen street.
T. Crowe. High street.
P. Doherty, Darling street.
C. Dewane, Darling street.
E. Gamble, Anne street
J. Gunning & Sons, Darling **street.**
J. Haren, Darling street.
C. Irwin, Belmore street.
R. Johnston, Market street
T. Kyle, Darling street.
A. Law, High street.
H. Lindsay, Townhall street.
J Little, Queen street.
P. Lilly, Townhall street.
J. Magrath, Belmore street.
J Maguire, Townhall street.
J. Martin, Townhall street.
E. Monaghan, Royal Hotel.
A. Moreton, Church street.
T. Mulligan, Dublin road.
D. M'Gaw, High street.
T. M'Grath, Townhall street.
J. M'Elgunn, Anne street,
P. M'Namee, Railway Hotel, **Fort**hill street.
F. O'Brien, Darling street.
J. Quinton, Church street
C. Shannon, Belmore street.
J. Shannon, Belmore street.
James Slavin, Townhall street.
C. M. Stewart, East Bridge street.
The Old Still, Townhall street—B. Reilly, manager,
G. Willis, Imperial Hotel, Townhall street.

SPOOL MILL.

M'Neill & Co., Mill street.

STEAM SAW MILLS.

Bradshaw & Co., East Bridge st.
R. Duffy, Forthill street.

TANNER AND CURRIER.
W. Lowery, Belmore street.

TAILORS & CLOTHIERS.
James Cavanagh, Wellington place.
W. R. Cooney, High street.
J. Robinson, High street.
W. Teele, Townhall street.

TIMBER MERCHANTS.
Bradshaw & Co., East Bridge street.
J Lemon, East Bridge street.

TOBACCO MANUFACTURER.
A. Cassidy, High street.

TOBACCONISTS.
G. Irvine, Darling street.
E. Rice, Darling street.

WHITE SMITHS,
Denis Maguire, Forthill street.
J. Maguire, Paget street.
Thomas Maguire, Quay Lane,
D Murphy, Brooke street.

WORK-MUSLIN FACTORY.
W. Galt and Co , Henry street.

Town Commissioners, Law Courts, &c.

Resident Magistrate—
Radolphus Harvey, Esq.
Borough Court Magistrate—
Extinct.
TOWN COMMISSIONERS—
Thomas R. Whitley, Chairman ;
James Coalter,
George Darragh,
James Dundas,
Edward Gamble,
Thomas Gordon,
James Kenny,
Thomas Kyle,
John Lemon,
James Maguire,
John Maguire,
James M'Elgunn,
Edward M'Nulty,
John Molyneux,
Edward Monaghan,
Thomas Plunket,
William Teele,
William Trimble,
Thomas Verner,
George Wadsworth.
George Willis,
Town Clerk—John Cleland.
Agent—Henry N. Lowe.
Borough Surveyor—John Wray.
Sanitary Officer—Dr. B. Gamble.
Sub-Sanitary Officer and Townhall
Keeper—William Dundas.
Town Sergeants—Andrew Brown,
and Edward Maguire.

LOCAL LAW COURTS.
Quarter Sessions and County Court—
Held in the County Courthouse.
Clerk of the Peace—Augustus T.
Jones, Esq.
Petty Sessions—Held in Co. Court-
house, on every Monday, at 12 o'ck.
Clerk—Mr. W. F. Jones
Borough Court—Extinct.
CONSTABULARY.
County-Inspector—Henry G. Cary,
Esq., Enniskillen.
SUB-INSPECTORS.
Enniskillen—
Lisnaskea—Wm. Mulloney, Esq.
Kesh—Richard M'Keane, Esq.
Derrygonnelly—
FERMANAGH COUNTY GAOL.
Enniskillen.
Visiting Committee meet first Monday
in each month.
Maurice C. Maude, Esq., J.P.
John Brady, Esq., J.P.
John A. Pomeroy, Esq., J.P.
Colonel J. G. Irvine.
Governor of Gaol—
E. H. T. Royse, Esq.
Dispensary, Wellington Place, open
Mondays and Thursdays from 10
a m. to 12 o'clock, noon. Medical
Officer—Dr. Baptist Gamble, Dar-
ling street.

Enniskillen Union.

Enniskillen Union (partly in Counties Fermanagh, Cavan and Tyrone) population in 1871, 43,542; 42 Electoral Divisions. Valuation, £106,315 The Board of Guardians meets on Tuesdays.

Chairman—The Right Hon. the Earl of Belmore, K.C.M.G., Castlecool e Enniskillen.

Vice-Chairman—George Black, Esq., 25 Church street, Enniskillen.

Deputy Vice-Chairman—George Weir, Esq., Gillyholm, Enniskillen.

Treasurer—Ulster Bank, Enniskillen.

Clerk and Returing Officer—William Henry Morrison.

Master and Matron—Alexander Price and Jane Scarlett.

Chaplains, { Church of Ireland—Rev. Samuel Greer, M.A. Roman Catholic—Very Rev. James M'Meel, P.P., D.D. Presbyterian—Rev. Alexander Cooper Maclatchy, A.M.

Medical Officer—Edward Bagot, F.R.C.S.I., L.K.Q.C.P.I.

Relieving Officers—Richard Maguire, Enniskillen; Rich. Bracken, Tattena-mona, Florencecourt.

Superintendent Registrar of Births, Deaths, and Marriages William Henry Morrison, Esq., Clerk of the Union.

Dispensary Districts, Population in 1871. Medical Officers and Registrars of Births, Deaths, and Marriages.

Ely—5,960, William Parke, L.R.C.S.I., L.R.C.P., Edinburgh.

Enniskillen—12,211, Baptist Gamble, L.R.C.S.I., L.K.Q.C.P.I.

Florencecourt—7,443, Edward Copelaud, L.R.C.S.I.

Holywell—8,437, Alexander Flood, L.R.C.S.I.

Lisbellaw—2,418, Thomas John Wilkin, L.R.C.S.I.

Tempo—7,130, Adam Clarke, L.R.C.S.I., L.K.Q.C.P.I.

Officers under the Public Health Act, 1874.

Executive Sanitary Officer—Clerk of the Union.

Consulting Sanitary Officer—Medical Officer of Enniskillen Dispensary District.

Sanitary Officers—Dispensary Medical Officers.

Sanitary Sub-Officers—Relieving Officers and John Nixon, Kiltomelly, Gortahill.

Local Government Board Officers.

Inspector—Richard T. Hamilton, Esq.

Auditor—R. H. Jephson, Esq.

LISNASKEA.

A MARKET town on the Great Northern Railway, in the Parish of Aughalurcher, Barony of Magherastaphena ; it lies 3 miles south by east of Maguiresbridge, $5\frac{1}{4}$ north north-west of Newtownbutler, and 9 south-east of Enniskillen. Very great improvements have been made in recent years by its noble Proprietor, The Earl of Erne, K.P., Custos Rotulorum of the county. Amongst the principal public buildings are—the Townhall, Public Dining Rooms, two good Hotels, first-class Corn, Butter, Pork, and Flax Markets ; a very handsome Branch of the Ulster Bank, a commodious Episcopalian Church, and a Methodist Preaching-House.

General Market Day—Saturday.

Market for the Sale of Flax, Pork and Fowl — Wednesday. Flax opens at 9 A.M. Pork opens at half past 10 o'clock.

Clerk of Markets—Mr. W. Graham.

Petty Sessions — fortnightly, except when that day happens on a Fair day, in such case there is an interval of three weeks.

Clerk of Petty Sessions — Mr. S. M. Huggard.

Delivery of Letters—7 A.M. & 2 P.M. Postmaster—Mr. Thos. Robinson.

Arrival of Up Trains to Dublin, Greenore, &c. (Passenger) — 6.40 A.M, 10.4 A.M., 1.35 P.M., and 4.55 P.M.

Down Trains—10.45 A.M., 12.50 P.M., and 6.30 P.M.

Protestant Clergy — Rev. W. C. Ledger, Incumbent ; Rev. C. J. Ward, Curate.

Roman Catholic—Rev. John Cassidy, P.P. ; Rev. James Hogan, C.C.

Registrar of Marriages—Mr. William Wherry ; Deputy—

Solicitor — T. C. Clarke, Esq., Munville.

Medical Officer of Dispensary and Workhouse—W. J. Sandles, M.D.

Ulster Bank Manager—Jas. Williss, Esq., open from 10 A.M. to 3 P.M.

Loan Fund Manager—Mr. William Wherry.

List of Shopkeepers. &c.

BAKERS—
Mr. James Fair.
„ William Forster
„ A. Magovern (Confectioner).
„ R. Masterson,
„ William Whittaker.
„ Henry Irwin.

CONFECTIONER AND NEWS AGENT.
Mrs. Anne Maguire.

DELPH SHOPS.
Mr. John M Clintock.
„ James Robinson.
Miss Wilson.

DELPH AND TOY SHOP.
Mr. Thomas Rennick.

FANCY AND DRAPERY—
Mr. J. H. Wilson.
„ A. W. Berry.
Messrs. Forster and Anderson.
Mrs. Thomas Rennick.
Mr. William Beatty.
„ William Faussett.
„ George Arnold.
Miss Wilson.
Mr. John Maguire.
„ Patrick M'Manus.
Misses Liddle.

GENERAL MERCHANTS—
Mr. Thomas Maguire.
Mr. Robert Masterson.
„ J. H. Wilson.
Messrs. Whitley Bros.

GROCERS AND PROVISION DEALERS.
Mr. Thomas Boland.
„ A Magovern.
„ John Bryson.
„ Samuel Maguire.
„ Francis M'Manus.

GROCERS, &c.—Continued.

Mr. Hugh M'Nulty.

„ James Phair.

„ Liddle Thompson.

Messrs. Whitley Bros.

WOOLLEN DRAPERS—

„ George Arnold

Mr. A. W. Berry.

Messrs. Forster and Anderson.

„ John Maguire.

„ Patrick M'Manns.

„ John H. Wilson,

PUBLICANS.

Mr. William Adams.

„ Moses Hall.

„ Robert Little.

„ Samuel Maguire.

„ Thomas Maguire.

„ Francis M'Manus.

„ Owen M'Manus.

„ Joseph Swann.

PUBLICANS—Continued,

Mr. William Richardson.

„ Liddle Thompson.

VICTUALLERS—

Mr. Charles Annon.

„ William Beatty.

GENERAL GROCERY AND PERFUMERY.

Mr. Archibald Noble.

VENDOR OF MEDICINES

Mr. Liddle Thompson.

HARDWARE MERCHANTS.

Mr. John M'Clintock.

„ Arthur Dunn

„ Robert Masterson.

„ J H. Wilson.

HOTEL PROPRIETORS.

Mr. Wm. Richardson.

„ J. H. Wilson,

LEATHER MERCHANTS.

Mr. Arthur Dunn.

„ William Richardson.

Lisnaskea Union.

Lisnaskea Union (County Fermanagh), population in 1871, 23,832 ; 20 Electoral Divisions. Valuation, £57,976. The Board of Guardians meets on Saturdays, at 12 o'clock.

Chairman—Earl of Erne, Crom Castle, Newtownbutler.

Vice-Chairman—Frederick S. Wrench, Esq , J.P., Lurganbrae, Brookeborough.

Deputy Vice-Chairman—John S. Murray, Esq., J.P., Mount Charles, Lisnaskea.

Treasurer—Ulster Bank, Lisnaskea.

Clerk and Returning Officer—Joseph O'R. Hoey.

Master and Matron—Alexander Fyfe and Jane Flanagan

Chaplains, { Church of Ireland—Rev. W. C. Ledger, A.M.
{ Roman Catholic—Rev. Peter Maguire.

Medical Officer—William J. Sandle, L.F.P.S., Glasgow, M.R.C.S.E.

Relieving Officers—David Patton, Mullyneeny, Derrylin; Alexander Beatty, Killykeeran, Brookeborough.

Superintendent Registrar of Births, Deaths, and Marriages.

Joseph O'R. Hoey, Esq., Clerk of Union.

Dispensary Districts, Population in 1871, Medical Officers and Registrars of of Births, Deaths, and Marriages.

Brookeborough—6,834, Richard Henry, M.D.

Derrylin—6,962, James Maxwell, M.D., L.R.C.S., Edinburgh.

Lisnaskea—6,026, William J. Sandle, L.F.P.S., Glasgow, M.R.C.S.E.

Maguiresbridge—3,142, Thomas Knox, L.R.C.S.I., L.M., L.K.Q.C.P.I.

Officers under the Public Health Act, 1874.

Executive Sanitary Officer—Clerk of the Union.

Consulting Sanitary Officer—Medical Officer of the Union.

Sanitary Officers—Dispensary Medical Officers.

Sanitary Sub-Officers—Relieving Officers.

Local Government Board Officers.

Inspector—Richard T. Hamilton, Esq.

Auditor—R. H. Jephson, Esq.

BELLEEK

Is a most prosperous and thriving little town in the parish of the same name, and in the Barony of Lurg. The Erne river, after escaping from Lough Erne, rolls swiftly 2½ miles to Belleek, and passing the prosperous and extensive porcelain works of Messrs D. M'Birney & Co., and there giving the aid of its powerful force in working their ponderous machinery, forms a noble cataract, equivalent in average mechanical power to 15,000 horses. The Railway from Bundoran to Enniskillen passes it. There are extensive lime and brick works in the neighbourhood, at Castlecaldwell. There is now a line of Railway from Castlecaldwell to Donegal contemplated, which, if completed, will greatly improve the trade, and develope the resources of Donegal and Fermanagh. The town is much resorted to in summer by tourists and anglers, as there is most excellent sport on the river, and the site of the town most picturesque and healthy, partly. it is presumed, in consequence of its proximity to Bundoran, the fashionable watering place, which is about five miles off. There is a Police Station, a Petty Sessions Court, and a Market House, and two excellent Hotels, one kept by a Mr Johnston, and the other by Mr. M'Hugh. There are several grocery establishments and other shops, and the Pottery of Messrs. M'Birney and Armstrong conduces largely to the prosperity of the town, in employing some hundreds of hands, the beauty and excellence of whose china and other wares is now known over the whole world to millions of people who do not know where Belleek is. Recently Mr. M'Birney has prochased the townlands containing Belleek and its surroundings, and considerable improvements have been made in the character of the residences, and dwelling-houses for workmen.

There are two Eel Weirs close to the town, and several ton weight of these fish have often been caught in less than an hour at night. Cliff, the delightfully detached residence of the Conolly family, is close to the town.

Names of Traders :—

Mr. Gallagher, licensed grocer.
W. Knox, postmaster, telegraph office and general dealer.
J. Moohan, baker and publican.
Miss Young, draper and milliner.
E, Greyson, publican.
D. Johnston, hotel keeper.
A. M'Hugh, hotel keeper and publican
J. Meehan, general dealer—butter, eggs and pork.
Mr. Walmsley, butcher.
Mrs. Kelly, fishing tackle dealer.
Mr. Martin, baker.
Mr. Quin, butcher.
Mrs. Donaldson, general dealer.
W. Garvan, publican.
Mr. Dolan, shoemaker.
Mr. M'Brien, do,
W. Irwin, Esq., dispensary surgeon, registrar, and sanitary referee.
J. Armstrong, process-server.
Mrs. Dolan, dressmaker.
Mr. M'Nulty, tailor.
Whitley, Brothers, general dealers.

BROOKEBOROUGH.

THIS neat little town, with a population of about 500, is situated on the main road, nearly mid-way between Lisnaskea and Five-miletown, the distance from the former being 4 and from the latter 5 Irish miles. Maguiresbridge, the nearest station on the Great Northern Railway, is $2\frac{1}{2}$ miles distant. The town consists of a row of regularly built, and with one or two exceptions slated houses, on each side of a straight wide street, well accommodated with footpaths. Colebrooke, the residence of the popular landlord, Sir Victor A. Brooke, Bart, in whose family the property has been for generations, is about two miles distant, from which circumstance, no doubt, the town originally derived its name. Viewed at a distance from any of the neighbouring heights it presents a somewhat picturesque appearance, owing to the fact that the adjacent elevated ground is wooded, the planting having been carried out with consumate good taste by the landlord. The places of worship in, or about the immediate vicinity of the town, are the Wesleyan Chapel, and the Roman Catholic Chapel, the Episcopel Church for the parish of Aghavea, in which Brookeborough is situated, being about $1\frac{1}{2}$ miles distant. There is no Presbyterian place of worship nearer than Maguiresbridge. The only other buildings of a public nature are the Court House, the Constabulary Barrack and a National School. The former is a large square block-building, in a pretty central position, the ground portion, with an arched entrance, serving the purpose of a Market House, while a large upper room is used as a Court House, in which a monthly Petty Sessions Court is held. There is also a smaller room in the building in which a Bank Agency from the Lisnaskea Branch of the Ulster Bank is conducted every Tuesday from eleven o'clock, a.m., until 2 p m. The Constabulary Barrack and National School are both neat buildings, and present externally, a somewhat ornamental style of architecture. The postal, arrangements are as follows :—A foot messenger carries the Mail from Lisnaskea, arriving at 8.30 a.m., the first delivery being at 9 o'clock. This messenger returns to Lisnaskea at 4 o'clock in the afternoon. A post car which runs between Fivemiletown and Lisnaskea passes Brookeborough at 11 a.m., taking up the first mails for Enniskillen and Londonderry on the one side, and Dublin on the other ; returning at 3 p.m., immediately after which there is a second delivery. The latest hours for posting letters are, for the morning post, 10.30 a.m., and for the afternoon post 3.45 p.m.

Names of Traders :—

CLERGYMEN.
Rev. A. M. Furlonge, A.M., Incumbent of Aghavea Parish
Rev. G. B. Sullivan, A.B., Curate, do
Rev. G. M. Clarke, Wesleyen Minister (Superintendent)
Rev. James M'Kenna, P.P.

DISPENSARY DOCTOR.
Richard Henry, Esq., A.B., M.D., Q.U.I., L.R.C.S.I.

BUILDERS.
Messrs. George & James Armstrong

BAKERS.
Edward Armstrong
J. Bredin

CARPENTERS.
John Bloomfield
James Gillespie

COOPER.
Robert Reid

COAL MERCHANTS.
Edward Armstrong
Charles Coulter
Samuel Murphy

DRAPERS.
Edward Armstrong
Charles Coulter
David Gillespie
Samuel Murphy

DELPH AND POTTERY.
William Johnston
Miss Joyce

GROCERS.
Miss J. Armstrong
Edward Armstrong
Miss Blakely
Charles Coulter
David Gillespie
Samuel Murphy
William Johnston

HOTEL KEEPER.
James Cassidy

LEATHER CUTTER.
Charles Coulter

MILLINERY AND DRESSMAKING.
Miss Baker

PUBLICANS.
James Cassidy
Miss Clarke
Charles Coulter

SHOEMAKERS.
William Armstrong
John M'Elroy
James M'Mahon

TIMBER MERCHANTS.
Edward Armstrong
Charles Coulter

TAILORS.
Joseph Kane
Peter M'Mahon

BALLINAMALLARD,

THE first station from Enniskillen to Derry, on the Great Northern Railway, is a small post town with about 320 of a population, lies about five miles from Enniskillen. It contains an Episcopalian Church, and Methodist Preaching House ; a Constabulary Barrack, two water-power Scutch Mills, and two Corn Mills. No Roman Catholic Chapel nearer than a mile and a half. The mails arrive at 6.0 a.m., and leave at 7.30 p.m.; Postmaster— James Patterson. Magheracross, the residence of George C. Lendrum, Esq., lies in the immediate vicinity, as does also Crocknacrieve, belonging to Lieutenant Archdale, R.N.

BELCOO.

BELCOO is, without exception one of the prettiest little villages in the county, lying, as it does, surrounded by hills, some of which presents a wild and stern aspect peculiar to those mountain districts, while immediately in front of it for a space of two miles stretches the beautiful waters of Lough Macnean, with its pretty islands. The village in the summer season presents as magnificent a view as parts of Killarney. Of the many pleasing objects to be seen about the neighbourhood, the charming residence of T. H. Jones, Esq., is one of the principal. Belcoo lies 9 miles north-west of Enniskillen, and is one of the principal stations on the new line of the Sligo, Leitrim, and Northern Counties Railway. A weekly Market for Pork, Butter, and other dairy produce, has lately been opened, and is already largely attended. The Sligo, Leitrim, and Northern Counties Railway at present provides a special train for the convenience of Marketers. The Monthly Fair, held on the 5th of each month, is generally well attended. The Railway runs through the prettiest portion of the surrounding country, under the foot of the Benmore Mountain, and for some distance close to the lake. The line is being rapidly constructed between here and its junction with the Midland Great Western, at Ballasadare, over which it will run into Sligo. Its next portion to Glenfarne is ready to open.

Names of Traders :—

Copeland John, Hamilton Arms Hotel, (Posting, &c.); Buchanan David; Grocer and Haberdasher ; Leonard John, Wine and Spirit Merchant; Maguire Patrick, Grocer and Spirit Dealer ; M'Cauley John, Butcher; Porteus John, Auctioneer and Valuator, General Posting Establishment, and Pork Dealer.

CHURCH HILL,

A village in the parish of Innismacsaint, Barony of Magheraboy. It stands on the old road, and a little west of a sweep of the new road, from Enniskillen to Ballyshannon 8 miles east-south-east of Belleek, and 9 north-west of Enniskillen. Its site is 4 or 5 furlongs west of the middle of the west margin of the Lower Lough Erne on the top of one of the numerous low ridges which rise summit over summit till they blend with the lofty hills of Shean and Glennlong. A little south of it are the small but romantic lakes of Carrick and Bunnahone, whose superfluent waters form-the Sillies rivulet. The old church, which gave name to the village, is now a ruin, and a new church has been built close to the Glebe-house and near the new road. The Church of Benmore was built by the joint efforts of the Rev. Hugh Hamilton, Rector, and John, second Marquis of Ely, in the year 1830-31.

DERRYGONNELLY,

A VILLAGE in the Parish of Innishmacsaint, Barony of Maheraboy, is seven miles north-west of Enniskillen, at the intersection of the mountain road thence to Garrison. with the road southward from Churchhill to Belcoo Bridge. There is a monthly fair held on the 24th of every month. There is a Constabulary Station, a Petty Sessions Court, and a Market House in the town ; an Episcopal Church, about 2 miles from it. a Roman Catholic Chapel a few perches outside, and in the town a Methodist Preaching House, two schools—one under the National Board of Education, and the other under Erasmus Smith's Board. There is an excellent Hotel, kept by Mrs Timony, from which a two-horse van leaves every Tuesday, Thursday, and Fair day of Enniskillen (10th of the month) for Enniskillen, as there is no railway communication. There are four houses where post cars can be had. There is also a branch of the Belfast Bank open here every Wednesday and Fair days.

Names of Clergymen and Traders :—

Clergymen—Rev. George Tottenham, Benmore, Episcopalian ; Rev. Michael T. Carney, P.P., Monea ; Rev. James Cullinan, C.C., Derrygonnelly ; Rev. C. North, methodist preacher, Church Hill ; Rev. J. Johnston, methodist preacher, Springfield.

Messrs. Breen Richard, draper ; Cocherane James, postmaster and grocer ; Carson John James, grocer and general dealer ; Hamilton William, leather cutter ; Kittson William, draper ; M'Brien John, merchant ; M'Caffry Michl, grocer and general dealer ; Parke Christopher, merchant ; Robinson William, merchant ; Timoney Eliza, hotel ; Weir Edward, grocer and general dealer, with ten public houses and a good many other small shops.

IRVINESTOWN.

THIS town, with a population of about 800, is situate on the Bundoran branch of the Great Northern Railway, has made rapid advances in late years, and bids fairly to become one of the best market towns in Fermanagh. Through the indefatigable exertions of Major Francis D'Arcy of Castle Irvine, markets for pork, flax, potatoes, butter, eggs, fowl, corn and other produce, have been so firmly established and so well governed that they are increasing every season. The Main street of the town is unequalled in many of the large, and in all of the small towns in Ulster, having a width of forty yards at its widest part. The side paths are flagged, and nearly ten feet wide, and forms a happy contrast to the generality of sidepaths in much larger places. A branch of the Northern Bank is for years established in this town, and is in a most flourishing state for a branch. The markets are held every Wednesday, and the fairs on the 8th of the month.

Castle Irvine, the seat of the D'Arcy Irvine family for several centuries, is within three-quarters of a mile of the town, and pleasantly situated in a prettily wooded portion of the demesne. It is a very handsome structure of modern times, internally decorated with all that art, wealth and taste could supply. The lands surrounding are exceedingly fertile, and the wealth of the people is chiefly derived from agriculture. The town Church of Irvinestown, capable of seating 600 persons, is an exceedingly pretty building. There are besides three other places of worship in the town—the Presbyterian Church, nearly opposite the Railway Station (erected 1832), and two Methodist Preaching-houses. There are two Roman Catholic Chapels outside the town, one, the parish Chapel—at Whitehill, the other at Coolaness, or " Lisaroo," as it is more generally called: There is also a Reading Room in Mill street, to which is attached a Refreshment Room. The National Schools in the town are two—one under Protestant patronage, the other under Roman Catholic—and both are well attended. Waterworks have been erected at a cost of between £700 and £800. The water comes from the townland of Moneykee, and was pronounced by Doctor Cameron on his analysis, as being remarkably free from all deleterious ingredients. The Union Workhouse affords accommodation for upwards of 500 inmates, it lies beyond the town from the Railway Station, healthfully situated on a rising ground almost fronting the Grand Gate to the Castle Irvine Demesne.

Names of Traders :—

Abercrombie John, Nailer, Back st.
Allen William, Cooper, Castle street
Anderson, J. K., Manager Northern Bank, Main street
Armstrong Wm., Publican, Main st.
Armstrong H. & T., Drapers, Main st.
Armstrong W.,Grocer, Fair Green st.

Beacom John, Tailor, Church street
Beacom Thos., Grocer, Pound street
Boheney Jas , Gardener, Castle Irvine
Bray Wm., Hotel Proprietor, Main st.
Brown John, Cooper, Fair Green st.
Brown J., Provision Dealer, Main st.
Brown Samuel, Cooper, Pound street

Campbell T., Baker & Grocer Main st.

Cassidy Thos., Butcher, &c., Rookery

Cassidy C., Butcher, Fair Green st.

Clarke R., Postmaster, Church street

Oochrane W., Provision Dealer, Main street

Cowan Benjamin, Draper, Main street

Curley B., Flaxdresser, Fair Green street

Curley C., Dealer, Fair Green street

Delaney J. M., Excise Officer, Castle street

Doherty Patrick, Tinsmith, Back st.

Doorish J., L. F. Bailiff, Pound street

Douglas Samuel, G. Merchant, Main street

Dudgeon, —, Draper, Main street

Fenton George, Saddler, Main street

French S., Cashier, Northern Bank, Castle street

Gallagher F., Spirit Merchant, Main street

Gallagher Miss, Dressmaker, P. street

Gardiner Mrs., China and Glass Dealer, Fair Green street

Gavigan P., Watchmaker, Main street

Gilmore Misses, Milliners, Main st.

Goane David, N. S. Teacher, Church street

Gormley John, Carpenter, Pound st.

Graham John, Stamp Distributor, Grocer and Seed Merchant, Main street

Graham Robert, Civil Bill Officer & Sexton, Church street

Gray John, Turner, Fair Green street

Hunter Thomas, Cooper, Castle street

Irvine William, Spirit Merchant, Main street

Johnston Robert, Draper and Ironmonger, Main street

Johnston William, General Grocer, Church street

Jolly Irvine, Spirit Merchant, Mill st.

Jolly Andrew, Spirit Merchant, Mill street

Jolly Hugh, Spirit Merchant, Main street

Kelly P., Boot Maker, Church street

Kerr Edward, Grocer, Main street

Keys Robert, General Smith, Castle street

Leonard James, Tailor, Pound street

Leonard T., Tailor, Fair Green st.

Maguire Archibald, Tailor, Pound st

Maguire A., N. S. Teacher, Main st.

Maguire John, Draper, Main street

Malcolmson T. R., do. do.

Maxwell Mrs., Pound street

M'Canny Thomas, Spirit Merchant and Carpenter, Main street

M'Clelland John, Ironmonger and Grocer, Main street

M'Coy James, Boot Maker, Main st

M'Coy Mrs, Grocer, Fair Green st.

M'Crory John, Carpenter, Main st.

M'Culgan John, Grocer, Main street

M'Donnell Hugh, S. Merchant, Main street

M'Grath W., C. Merchant, Main st.

M'Guigan Nicholas, Carpenter, Main street

M'Hugh John, Draper, Main street

M'Kenna P., Confect., Church street

M Keone Mrs. L., H. Keeper, Castle street

M'Loughlin John, Grocer, Main st.

M'Loughlin F., Publican, Main st.

M'Morris Thos, Grocer, Main street

Morris R. H., Auctioneer, Insurance Agent, and Petty Sessions Clerk

Murphy J., Bootmaker, Church st.

O'Brien John, Butcher and Spirit Merchant, Main street

O'Brien Michael, Publican, Main st.

O'Flanagan J., Publican, Pound st.

O'Gorman George, Publican, and Draper, Main street

O'Reilly Hugh, Butcher, Main street

O'Reilly Hugh, jun., Butcher, Fair Green street

O'Reilly Daniel, Butcher, Main st.

Rankin Adam, Baker, Main street

Rinchey Mrs., Fair Green street

Rinchey Joseph, Farmer, Back street

Robinson W., Grocer, Main street

Scott William, Car Builder, Castle st.

Shackleton W. H., Timber Merchant, Castle street

Simpson George, Watchmaker and Summons-Server, Castle street

Sproule Fras., Grocer, Main street

Tumath Christopher, Spirit Merchant, Main street

Valentine John, Smith, Church street

Vance William, Farmer, Main street

Wilson Robert, Teacher, Church st.

Young Anthony, Miller, Back street

Young Thos., Mason, Back street

Clergymen—Irish Church, Revs. R. Verschoyle, M.A., Derryvullen Rectory; J. W. Gallagher, The Manse, Irvinestown. Roman Catholic—Rev. Hugh Maguire, Whitehill; Rev. Thos. Power, Whitehill. Presbyterian—Rev. James M Kee, The Manse, Irvinestown Methodists—Rev. James Daly, The Commons, Irvinestown; Revs. J. J. Hutchinson and Matthew Hazley, Main street, Irvinestown.

Medical—Dr. Alexander Irvine, Eglinton Lodge, Irvinestown.

Irvinestown Union.

Irvinestown Union (County Fermanagh), 18 Electoral Divisions. The Board of Guardians meet on Wednesdays.

Chairman—Captain Mervyn Edward Archdale, Castle Archdale, Lisnarick, Enniskillen.

Vice-Chairman—Major Francis D'Arcy, Castle Irvine, Irvinestown.

Deputy Vice-Chairman—Gerard Irvine. Esq., Feglish, Irvinestown.

Treasurer—Northern Bank, Irvinestown.

Clerk and Returning Officer—Christopher Graham.

Master and Matron—James Armstrong and Isabella Johnston.

Chaplains—Irish Church, Rev. R. Verschoyle; Roman Catholic, Rev. Hugh Maguire, P.P.

Medical Officer—Alexander Irvine, M.D.

Relieving Officer—Robert Clarke, Irvinestown.

Superintendent Registrar of Births, Deaths and Marriages — Christopher Graham, Clerk of Union.

LISBELLAW,

A SMALL town in the barony of Tyrkennedy, on the Great Northern Railway, by the road it is 3 miles from Maguiresbridge, and 4 south-east of Enniskillen. It has latterly very much increased in size and improved in appearance, owing to the buildings and improvements made by its present owner, John G. V. Porter, Esq., of Belleisle. A water supply and fountains through the street is at present in course of progress, altogether it is a pleasant and fast improving place. There are three fairs held in the year, May 11, June 20, and November 11, and it is the site of an Episcopalian Church, a Presbyterian Meeting House, two Methodist Preaching Houses, a Roman Catholic Chapel, a District Dispensary, a Market

House, National Schools, and an Orange Hall. There is a comfortable hotel kept by Mr Beatty; also an extensive Woollen Factory at the end of the town, owned and wrought by Messrs. Henderson, and Eadie and doing a most prosperous and profitable business as evidenced by their additions in buildings and machinery. Messrs. Whitley Brothers, the extensive merchants of Enniskillen, have here one of their numerous and prosperous branch establishments, for sale of groceries, provisions, &c. There is also a Constabulary Barrack, and Court of Petty Sessions, and there is a Post Office with Savings Bank, Money Order and Postal Telegraph Office attached.

Names of Clergymen and Traders :—

Clergymen.—The Rev. R. M'Gregor, B. A., Incumbent of Lisbellaw; the Rev. T. S. Graham, A. M., Presbyterian Minister. Dispensary Doctor—Dr. Wilkin. Postmaster—Mr James M'Farland. Petty Sessions Clerk—Mr John Elliott. Hotel Proprietor—Mr. John Betty. Publicans—Mr. John Betty, Mr. James M'Creery. General Merchants—Messrs. Whitley Brothers, and Joseph Moore. Draper—Mr. Joseph Whitley. Bakers—Mr Joseph Moore and Mr. Robert Moore. Groceries—Messrs. Whitley Brothers, Joseph Moore, John M'Gaghy, Robert Moore. Mr. F. Ernest Power. Sub-Editor, *Lisbellaw Gazette*, Carrick House.

NEWTOWNBUTLER.

NEWTOWNBUTLER, a small post town in the parish of Galloon and barony of Coole, situate in the most flourishing district of the county, is distant from Clones 4 miles, from Cavan 11, Belturbet 7, from Lisnaskea 5, from Lanesborough Lodge, the summer residence of the Earl of Lanesborough, three miles, and from Crom Castle, the residence of the Earl of Erne, 3 miles. The town is the property of the Earl of Lanesborough. A large sum has been expended by the last and present Earl on the improvement of the town, in drainage, pumps, side paths, buildings, &c., and the town presents a clean and thriving appearance. The Episcopal Church situate on an eminence in the north-east of the town, is a fine building, with a square tower. The Roman Catholic Chapel in the south end is large and spacious. There are two Methodist Churches in the town and two National Schools. The neat, well-kept and commodious hotel (Lanesboro' Arms), of Mrs Reilly, is a great accommodation to travellers from north-west to the east of Ireland. An annual fair is held on the 12th of May, and a market every Tuesday. The town, which contains a population of about 500 inhabitants, is a station on the Great Northern Railway. Newtownbutler is a Quarter Sessions Division of the county. The

Petty Sessions are held on the second Wednesday in each month, James Cooke, Clerk. A branch of the Northern Bank is open on Tuesdays. Letters are delivered twice daily at 7.30 a.m., and 12.30 noon. Miss Clarke, postmistress   The Dispensary is open on every Monday and Friday ; Francis Creighton Fitzgerald, Dispensary Doctor.   Petty Sessions second Wednesday in every month.   Clergy — Rev. A. Jagoe, A.M., Episcopal ; Rev. H. Ward, P.P. ; Rev. Martin Hynds, Methodist Preacher.

Name of Traders :—

Adams Miss, grocer, and haberdasher ; Beatty Joseph, general merchant ; Courtney James, merchant and publican ; Hopkins William, grocer and white-smith ; Johnston James, draper and general merchant ; Larkin Mr., grocer ; Maguire John, merchant and publican ; Mowen Bernard. merchant and publican ; M'Grorty Mr., grocer ; Reilly Mr., merchant and publican.   Manure Agents—Beatty Joseph (for Richardson, Bros. & Co.); Beatty Nat. C (for Dublin and Wicklow Co.) ; Johnston James (for Goulding's.)   Hotel—Reilly Mrs., Lanesborough Arms.   Shipping Agents—Beatty N. C., American Line ; Johnston James, Cunard Line ; Maguire John, White Star Line ; Reilly Mr, Guion Line.   Tailors—M'Manus Patrick, Reilly Michael, Sheridan John. Carpenters—Armstrong John, Gilleece John, Hand Thomas.   Farrier—Morrow Robert   Dressmakers—Gregg Miss, M'Quilkin Mrs   Architect—Maguire James.   Shoemakers—Bell Pat, Daily William. M'Elroy James, M'Donald James, Robinson John, Nicholl John.   Wheelright—Moynagh Edward.   Bakery—Johnston James   Coal Merchants—Beatty Joseph, Johnston, James.   Hardware—Beatty Joseph, Johnston James   Agricultural Implement Agent—Beatty Nat. C.   News Agents—Beatty N. C., *Lisbellaw Gazette ;* Hopkins William, *Daily Express* ; M'Gorty William, *Freeman* and *Advocate* ; Purcell Miss, *Christian Herald.*

PETTIGO.

A VILLAGE, partly in the parish of Drumkeeran, Barony of Lurg, county Fermanagh, but chiefly in the parish of Templecarne, barony of Tyrhugh, county Donegal. It stands on the rivulet Termon, on the road from Belleek to Castle Derg, and on the east road from Enniskillen to Donegal, one mile north of the nearest part of Lower Lough Erne, 3½ south by east of Lough Derg, 4½ west-north-west of Kesh, 14 south-east by east of Donegal, 16 north-north-west of Enniskillen, and 96 north-north-west of Dublin. It stands amidst pretty green and wooded hills ; and its vicinity offers various fine vantage grounds for obtaining a panoramic view of the basin of Lower Lough Erne. The village contains a Church, a Presbyterian Meeting House, and a Roman Catholic Chapel. It is a prosperous and improving place. and possesses not a little notoriety as the great thoroughfare of the crowds of pilgrims who frequent Lough Derg. The Dispensary here is within the Donegal Poor Law Union. A Court of Petty Sessions is held on the last Friday of every month. A Fair is held on the 20th day of every month ; and a Market on every Monday in each week. There is a very commodious and well-kept Hotel and Posting establishment in the town, kept by Mr. Aiken, where tourists or other travellers (who are very numerous in Summer), are well accommodated on their way. It also contains a Wesleyan Chapel.

Names of Traders :—

Messrs Aiken Thomas, hotel keeper and draper ; Aiken Johnston, spirit merchant ; Armstrong, Mrs, draper and postmistress ; Elliott James, grocer ; Elliott John, grocer ; Falls John, grocer and baker ; Flood Patrick, spirit merchant ; Funston David. spirit merchant ; Gallagher Francis, draper ; Gillmor John, grocer ; M'Brien, Henry, draper and grocer ; M'Caffrey John, grocer ; M'Grath Mrs.. grocer ; M'Hugh Roderick, spirit merchant ; Read John, grocer ; Read Robert, grocer and hardware merchant ; Robinson, Hamilton, grocer, Tiernan John, spirit merchant ; Thompson Miss. draper and milliner.

ROSSLEA.

ROSSLEA is a village situate in the north-east part of the county, in the barony of Clonkelly. It contains 68 families, having a total population of 377. The river Finn, one of the tributaries of Lough Erne, which rises in Slieve Beigh mountain, passes through the village. The public buildings are one Roman Catholic Church, to which is attached a female National School, also a small Female National School, a Steam Flax Mill, a Corn Mill, a Medical Dispensary and Registry Office open on Tuesdays and Fridays, when Alexander Knight, Esq., M.D., Etna Lodge, is in attendance. There are also a Market House and Petty Sessions Court House and Constabulary Station. There is a fair held upon the 8th of each month for the sale of cattle and sheep. There is also a weekly market on Wednesdays for the sale of butter, eggs and fowl. Rosslea Manor, the residence of John Madden, Esq., is quite convenient to the village.

Names of Traders :—

Hannah Keenan, hotel keeper ; Joseph Callaghan, grocer and cattle dealer ; Edward Callaghan, grocer, and fowl dealer ; John M'Manus, baker and grocer; Robert Martin, boot and shoemaker ; John Cassidy, publican ; John Deering, hotel-keeper ; Francis Mulligan, grocer ; Mary M'Phillips, grocer ; John Graham, blacksmith ; Michael Murray, publican ; Thomas Cosgrove. publican ; Edward Callen, grocer : Thomas Keon, publican and blacksmith ; James Cox, postmaster, draper and milinery establishment : John Leordner, drapery establishment ; Robert Murray, publican and grocer ; John Bredin, painter and glazier ; Wm. Benson, boot and shoemaker ; John Magilly, boot and shoemaker : Thomas Murphy, tailor and outfitter.

EDERNEY

Is a thriving village on the principal roads from Enniskillen to Castlederg, and from Ballyshannon to Omagh, nearly midway between those towns. It is 5 miles from Irvinestown, and 2 from Kesh, at each of which there is a Railway Station. It has now a population of about 400. The Market is held every Thursday, and Fairs on the 17th of each month. There is a very fine Townhall, Masonic Lodge Room, Constabulary Barrack, Post Office, Scutch Mill worked by Steam, and Market Place. Water is supplied by fountains placed in the street. The houses are mostly slated, and the town lying among trees has a comfortable and picturesque appearance. The Northern Bank has a sub-office here, which is open every Thursday. There are two Schools, under the National Board of Education. There is also a Dispensary, attended by J. B. Graham, M.D., T.C.D., and L.R.C.S.I.

Clergymen (Church of Ireland) Rev. E. M. Weir, Incumbent. Magheraculmoney. Roman Catholic—Rev John O'Reilly, P.P.; Rev. Peter Meigan, Administrator; Rev. John Maguire, C.C.

Names of Traders :—

BUILDER.
John Ellis & Son.

CARPENTER.
Daniel Hicks.

DRAPERS.
Thos. Drewrey.
Miss Knox.
Wm. Murphy.
John Maguire.
F. S. M'Morrow.

DRESSMAKERS.
Miss Monaghan.
Mrs. Reid.

GROCERS.
James Barret.
Thomas Knox.
James Mulhern.
Miss Tiernan.

HARDWARE, &c.
John Maguire.
Wm. Murphy.

LEATHER CUTTERS.
John Maguire.
Wm Murphy.

MILLINERY.
Mrs. Maguire.
Miss Murphy.
Miss Knox
Miss Drewery.
Mrs. M·Murrow.
William Frith.
James Graham.
Hugh Gallagher.

PUBLICANS.

SHOEMAKERS.
Francis Gallagher.
Wm. Irvine.
Bernard Maguire.
Wm. Reilly.

TAILORS.
James Judge.
Wm. Harvey.

LACK,

THE most northerly village in the county, is situated on the road from Ballyshannon to Omagh, being about 11 miles from the latter town, it is 6 miles north of Irvinestown. 5 miles from Kesh, and lies in a valley among heath covered hills. Close to it is the summit level between the sea at Londonderry and Bally-shannon. The hills in the neighbourhood abound in game. It contains 25 houses with a population of 130. A Petty Sessions Court is held here, and there is a Constabulary Barrack, Post Office, National Schoolhouse, a Scutch Mill, and 3 Public Houses. A Loan Fund Bank, open every fourth Friday in the month, from 11 a.m. till 3 p m, Thomas Belton, Esq., Actuary. There is also a Dispensary, open every Thursday from 10 a.m. till 2 p.m., attended by Dr. J. B. Graham, Drumrush House. Good Water is supplied in Fountains, brought by pipes from a spring in the adjacent hill of Largy. The road from here to Ederney is one of the finest in the county, and evidences of an improving Londlord is everywhere to be seen in the neighbourhood. Within the past year several comfortable houses have been built by Colonel Irvine, and they are all occupied. There is only one Resident Clergyman in the District, Rev. E. M. Weir, Incumbent, C. I.

Names of Traders :—

Mr. Thomas Miller, Publican and Draper; Mr. Porter, Shoemaker; Mr. Terence M'Mulkin, Smith ; Mr. Virtue, Postmaster.; Mr. Wm. Johnston Publican; Mr. Irvine Armstrong, Publican ; Mr. Patrick Cory. Grocer; Mr. Francis M'Intyre, Grocer; Mrs. Sunter, Grocer ; Mr. Patrick Maguire, Grocer.

MAGUIRESBRIDGE.

THIS town is one of the oldest in Fermanagh ; it contains a popu-lation of about 600, and is situated on the Great Northern Rail-way ; the Colebrooke River runs through it, and adds very much to the appearance and comfort of the place. It derives its name from a Bridge which spans the River, almost in the centre of the town. It is $2\frac{3}{4}$ miles south-west of Brookeborough, $2\frac{3}{4}$ north west of Lisnaskea, $2\frac{1}{4}$ of Lisbellaw, 5 of Tempo, and 7 of Enniskillen. The places of worship in it, and its vicinity are the Episcopalian Church, the Roman Catholic Chapel, the Presbyterian Meeting House, and the Methodist Chapel. There is a Police Barrack, two Schools under the National Board, and a Market House. There is no Townhall, but a room in the Market House serves the purpose when required. For some years past there has been no Market but we are informed that a Butter and Egg Market will be opened in a short time.

Delivery of Mails 8.30 a m. ; Postmaster—Mr. J. Irvine. Arrival of Up Trains, to Dublin, Greencre. &c. (Passenger) 6.30 a.m., 9.55 a.m., 1.30 p m , 4.35 p.m ; Down Trains, 10 50 a.m., 12.55 p.m.. and 6.35 p.m. Protestant Clergy—Rev. John Charlton, Presbyterian ; Rev. Wm. Maguire, and Daniel Henderson, Methodist. Roman Catholic—Rev. James Hogan. Medical Officer—Thomas Knox, Esq., M.D.

Names of Traders :—

AUCTIONEER.

Hugh Bell,

BAKERS.

Noble Brady.
Samuel Lough.
William Pratt.
Francis Naan.

CARPENTER.

Mr. Trotter.

DELPH SHOP.

Miss Joyce.

DRAPERS.

Mr. M'Dowal.
Mr. Law.
Mr. M'Manus.
Mr. Hamilton.
Miss Rachel Joyce.

FOWL DEALERS

Matthew Farry.
John Fife.
Tem Davis.

GENERAL MERCHANTS.

Samuel C. Lough.
Edward Law.
Noble Brady.
John Doonan.

GROCERS.

Mrs. Potts.
Mrs. M'Gowan.

GROCERS.—(Continued.)

Mrs. M'Intyre.
Mrs. Johnston.
William Pratt.
J. Hamilton.
P. M'Adams.
John Foster.

HOTEL.

Noble Brady.

PAINTER & GLAZIER.

Mr. M'Cullagh.

PROCESS-SERVER.

James Bogue.

PUBLICANS.

A. M'Aloon.
Michael Lynch.

SCHOOLMASTERS.

Mr. Taylor.
Mr. O'Berne.

SHOEMAKERS

J Breddin.
J. M'Awinnie.
P. Graham.
T. Connolly.

SMITH.

John Ferris

TAILORS.

P. M'Manus.
P. M'Alarnie.

TEMPO,

A VILLAGE in the Parish of Enniskillen and Barony of Tyrkennedy, stands on the Tempo rivulet, adjacent to the beautiful
demesne and handsome mansion house of the late Sir W. W. E.
Tennent, Bart. It is 6 miles from Enniskillen. The village is
clean and comfortable. There are good monthly Fairs held on
the 28th of each month. Has a Church, a Chapel, a Presbyterian
Meeting House, a Dispensary, a Post Office, a couple of Good
Inns, and a Constabulary Barrack. There are several good shops
and on the whole, there are few villages for miles around it
where the people seem to possess and enjoy prosperity more than
they do in Tempo.

Clergymen.—Church of Ireland—Rev. Mr. Morrow, Incumbent. Roman
Catholic—Rev. Mr. Loughran. P.P. ; Rev. Mr. Trainor, C.C. Presbyterian—
Rev. D. Clements.
Dispensary Doctor—Dr. Adam Clarke, Esq.

Names of Traders :—

Armstrong Rebecca, draper and milliner.

Beatty James, hotel, grocer & wine merchant, leather, &c.

Beatty Thomas, (P.L.G.) grocer, seed merchant, and postmaster.

Bogue Ellen, draper, china and glass warehouse, &c.

Brennan Michael, wine and spirit merchant, bakery and flour stores.

Britton Joseph, blacksmith.

Brady Patrick, nailor.

Beatty Andrew, boot and shoemaker.

Cooper James & Co, grocer and merchant.

Crawford James, grocer.

Connolly Thomas, boot & shomaker.

Donnelly James, publican.

Doran John, grocer.

Elliott William, corn and saw mills, merchant and agent for *Lisbellaw Gazette.*

Grey Patrick, tailor.

Gibson Mary, draper.

Hunter & Co., butter & egg merchants.

Little Ellen, grocer & delph merchant.

Mills James, grocer and baker.

Miller George A, publican.

Maguire Mary,   do.

Maguire Thomas,   do.

Maguire Lititia, grocer.

Maguire Andrew, (P.L.G.) agent for shipping companies.

Murphy John, tailor.

M'Manus Patrick, grocer, flour and meal stores.

M'Meniman Francis, publican.

M'Swiggan J., butter & egg merchant.

M'Reigney James, coachbuilder.

M'Reigney Arthur, blacksmith.

M'Caffrey John, cooper.

M'Dermott Thomas, cooper & grocer.

M'Callan Patrick, carpenter.

M'Cabe Patrick, boot & shoemaker.

M'Cann Owen,   do.

Owens Edward, butcher.

Shannon James, tailor.

Watson Thomas J., grocer, hardware and general merchant.

Watson Robert, druggist.

Warnock William, publican.

KESH

Is on the line of Railway from Enniskillen to Bundoran. The population is 296. There is a Fair held on the 4th of each month and a Corn Market every Friday. There is a Post Office and Money Order and Telegraph Office ; a Petty Sessions Court, and a Police Barrack. Kesh is 4 miles from Pettigo, 4 from Irvinestown, 2 from Ederney, and within a quarter of a mile of the lake shore. There is a Loan Fund Bank which is open every Friday. The landlords of the place are—William Archdale, Esq., M P., and the Governors of Vaughan's Charity. A Mail car runs daily through Kesh, from Omagh to Bundoran. There are no places of worship in Kesh.

Names of Traders :—

Hotel—Aiken William ; Draper — Aiken John ; Innkeepers — Campbell Mrs., Eaves Adam, Muldoon Tom ; Grocers—Elliott Richard, Gilmore Mrs., Humphrys Royal ; Baker—Kelly Bernard ; Smiths—Coulter Alexander, Irwin Henry ; Carpenter—M'Clintock William ; Postmaster—Aiken James.

PETTY SESSIONS COURTS

AND POLLING PLACES, CO. FERMANAGH.

Name of Petty Sessions Districts, and which are also the Polling Districts and Polling Places.	Acres.	Population.	Names of Clerks.	Number of Electors for 1880.	Day of holding Petty Sessions.
Belleek, -	32,558	5,475	Willliam Knox, -	249	Second Tuesday every month.
Brookeborough,	34,019	6,837	Joseph Swanwick,	259	First Tuesday in every month.
Derrygonnelly,-	43,194	5,909	James M'Keague,	390	Last Friday in every month.
Derrylin, -	33,066	8,968	Arthur Thomson,	431	First Wednesday in every month.
Enniskillen,	29,525	12,132	W. F. Jones, -	430	On every Monday.
Irvinestown,	44,017	12,345	Robert H. Morris,	261	Every Alternate Friday.
Kesh, -	25,316	5,842	James Aiken, -	349	First Tuesday every month.
Lack, -	25,886	4,465	David Miller, -	205	First Friday every month.
Letterbreen,	51,561	7,826	William H. Wilson,	556	Last Saturday every month.
Lisbellaw,-	25,912	6,097	John Elliott, -	465	Third Friday every month.
Lisnaskea,	17,527	5,206	Stephen M. Huggard,-	258	2nd & 4th Saturdays each month.
Newtownbutler,	38,314	9,090	James Cooke, -	563	Second Wednesday every month.
Rosslea, -	18,304	4,750	Joseph Graydon,	162	Fourth Saturday every month,
Total.........	457,195	92,794		4,778	

Days for Opening General Quarter Sessions and County Court Sittings, for the following Counties, for the year 1880.

Counties and Towns.	Hilary.	Easter.	Trinity.	Michaelmas.
Armagh—				
Ballybot ...	'79 30th Dec.	31st March.	15th June.	5th Oct.
Markethill ...	5th January.	5th April.	21st June	13th Oct.
Newtownhamilton			18th June.	
Armagh ..	13th January.	14th April.	28th June.	20th Oct.
Lurgan ...	8th January.	8th April.	24th June.	25th Oct.
Cavan—				
Ballyconnell ...		12th April.		15th Oct.
Cavan ...	6th January.	5th April.	8th June.	8th Oct.
Cootehill ...	2nd January.	31st March.	4th June.	5th Oct.
Bailiborough ...	'79 30 Dec.		1st June.	
Donegal—				
Ballyshannon..			15th June.	
Donegal ...	7th January.	29th March.	18th June.	11th Oct
Cardonagh ..	15th January.			
Buncrana ...			26th June.	
Glenties ...		5th April.		
Letterkenny ...		7th April.		20th Oct.
Lifford ...	20th January.	17th April.	1st July.	30th Oct.
Fermanagh—				
Newtownbutler	'79 30th Dec.	30th March.	16th June.	18th Oct.
Enniskillen ...	5th January.	5th April.	21st June.	25th Oct.
Leitrim—				
Carrick-on-Shannon	14th January.	21st April.	15th June	27th Oct.
Manorhamilton ...	21st January.	24th April.	22nd June.	20th Oct.
Ballinamore ...		14th April.		29th Oct.
Londonderry—				
Magherafelt ...	6th January.	31st March.	11th June.	9th Oct.
Coleraine ...	13th January.	7th April.	18th June.	18th Oct.
Limavady ...		15th April.		25th Oct.
Londonderry ...	20th January.	19th April.	25th June.	28th Oct.
Monaghan—				
Carrickmacross		5th April.		16th Oct.
Castleblayney...	'79 29th Dec.	6th April.	21st June.	18th Oct.
Clones ...	3rd January		26th June.	
Monaghan ...	5th January.	12th April.	28th June.	23rd Oct.
Tyrone—				
Dungannon ...	'79 31st Dec.	31st March.	22nd June.	6th Oct.
Strabane ...	8th January.	8th April.	29th June.	14th Oct.
Clogher ...	12th January.	12th April.	2nd July.	18th Oct.
Omagh ...	14th January.	14th April.	5th July.	20th Oct.

List of Post Towns and Money Order Offices in Fermanagh.

Name of Office.	Head Office.	Nearest Money Order Office.
Arney -	Enniskillen -	Florencecourt
Ballinamallard -	Omagh -	Irvinestown
Ballycassidy -	Do -	Enniskillen
Ballyreagh -	Enniskillen -	Do
Belleek * -	Omagh -	Money Order Office
Blaney -	Enniskillen -	Derrygonnelly
Boho -	Do	Blacklion
Brookborough -	Clones -	Money Order Office
Churchhill -	Do	Derrygonnelley
Clonelly -	Omagh -	Kesh
Derrygonnelly * -	Enniskillen -	Money Order Office
Derryharney -	Do	Lisbellaw
Derrylin -	Belturbet -	Ballyconnell
Drumane -	Enniskillen -	Enniskillen
Drumcose -	Do	Do
Ederney -	Omagh -	Money Order Office
Enniskillen * -	Head Office -	Do
Florencecourt -	Enniskillen -	Do
Garrison -	Omagh -	Belleek
Garvery -	Enniskillen -	Enniskillen
Irvinestown * -	Omagh -	Money Order Office
Kesh * -	Do -	Do
Killadeas -	Do -	Irvinestown
Lack -	Do -	Kesh
Leggs -	Do -	Belleek
Letterbreen -	Enniskillen -	Enniskillen
Lisbellaw * -	Do -	Money Order Office
Lisnarrick -	Omagh -	Irvinestown
Lisnaskea * -	Clones -	Money Order Office
Magheramena -	Omagh -	Belleek
Maguiresbridge -	Clones -	Money Order Office
Monea -	Enniskillen -	Derrygonnelly
Newtownbutler -	Clones -	Money Order Office
Roscor -	Omagh -	Belleek
Rossinver -	Do -	Do
Tamlaght -	Enniskillen -	Enniskillen
Tempo * -	Do -	Money Order Office

Telegraph Offices marked thus (*).

SELECTED POETRY.

Love in a Cottage.

They may talk of love in a cottage,
    And bowers of trellised vine—
Of nature bewitchingly simple,
    And milkmaid half divine ;
They may talk of the pleasure of sleeping
    In the shade of a spreading tree,
And a walk in the fields at morning,
    By the side of a footstep free !

But give me a sly flirtation
    By the light of a chandelier—
With music to play in the pauses,
    And nobody very near :
Or a seat on a silken sofa,
    With a glass of pure old wine,
And mamma too blind to discover
    The small white hand in mine.

Your love in a cottage is hungry,
    Your vine is a nest for flies—
Your milkmaid shocks the Graces,
    And simplicity talks of pies !
You lie down to your shady slumber
    And wake with a fly in your ear,
And your damsel that walks in the morning
    Is shod like a mountaineer,

True love is at home on a carpet,
    And mightily likes his ease—
And true love has an eye for a dinner,
    And starves beneath shady trees.
His wing is the fan of a lady,
    His foot's an invisible thing
And his arrow is tipped with a jewel,
    And shot from a silver string.

St. Patrick.

A Fig for St Dennis of France,
    He's a trumpery fellow to brag on ;
A fig for St George and his lance,
    Which spitted a heathenish dragon.
And the Saints of the Welshman or Scot,
    Are a couple of pitiful pipers,
Both of whom may just travel to pot,
    Compared with the patron of swipers,—
    St. Patrick of Ireland, my dear !

He came to the Emerald Isle
  On a lump of a paving-stone mounted ;
The steamboat he beat to a mile,
  Which mighty good sailing was counted.
Says he, ' The salt-water, I think,
  Has made me most bloodily thirsty,
So bring me a flagon of drink
    To keep down the mullegrubs, burst ye !
    Of drink that is fit for a saint !

He preach'd then with wonderful force,
  The ignorant natives a teaching ;
With a pint he wash'd down his discourse
  ' For,' says he, ' I detest your dry preaching.''
The people, with wonderment struck, :
  At a pastor so pious and civil,
Exclaimed, ' We're for you my old buck,
    And we pitch our blind gods to the devil.
    Who dwells in hot water below.'

This ended, our worshipful spoon
  Went to visit an elegant fellow,
Whose practice each cool afternoon,
  Was to get most delightfully mellow.
That day, with a black jack of beer,
  It chanced he was treating a party ;
Says the Saint, This good day, do you hear,
  I drank nothing to speak of my hearty ;
    So give me a pull at the pot.'

The pewter he lifted in sport
  (Believe me I tell you no fable),
A gallon he drank from the quart,
  And then planted it full on the table.
' A miracle !' every one said,
  And they all took a haul at the stingo :
They were capital hands at the trade,
  And drank till they fell ; yet by jingo !
    The pot still froth'd over the brim.

Next day, quoth his host, ' 'Tis a fast,
  But I've not in my larder but mutton ;
And on Fridays who'd make such repast,
  Except an unchristian-like glutton ?'
Says Pat, ' Cease your nonsense, I beg,
  What you tell me is nothing but gammon ;
Take my compliments down to the leg,
  And bid it come hither a salmon !'
    And the leg most politely complied.

You've heard, I suppose, long ago,
  How the snakes in a manner most antic,
He march'd to the county Mayo,
  And trundled them into the Atlantic.

Hence not to use water for drink
  The people of Ireland determine ;
With mighty good reason I think,
  Since St. Patrick has filled it with vermin,
    And vipers, and other such stuff.

Oh ! he was an elegant blade,
  As you'd meet from Fair Head to Kilcrumper,
And though under the sod he is laid,
  Yet here goes his health in a bumper !
I wish he was here that my glass
  He might by art magic replenish ;
But as he is not, why, alas !
  My ditty must come to a finish,
    Because all the liquor is out.

The Town of Passage.

The town of Passage
Is both large and spacious,
And situated
  Upon the say ;
'Tis nate and dacent,
And quite adjacent,
To come from Cork
  On a summer's day.
There you may slip in
To take a dippin'
Forenent the shippin'
  That at anchor ride ;
Or in a wherry
Cross o'er the ferry
To Carrigaloe
  On the other side.
Mud cabins swarm in
This place so charmin',
With sailors' garments
  Hung out to dry ;
And each abode is
Snug and commodious,
With pigs melodious,
  In their strawbuilt sty.
'Tis there the turf is
And lots of murphies,
Dead sprats, and herrings,
  And oyster shells ;
Nor any lack oh !
Of good tobacco,
Though what is smuggled
  By far excels.

There are ships from Cadiz
And from Barbadoes,
But the leading trade is
  In whisky punch ;
And you may go in
Where one Molly Bowen
Keeps a nate hotel
  For a quiet lunch.
But land or deck on
You may safely reckon,
Whatsoever country
  You come hither from,
Or an invitation
To a jollification
With a parish priest,
  That's called ' Father Tom.'
Of ships there's one fixt,
For lodging convicts—
A floating ' stone jug'
  Of amazing bulk ;
The hake and salmon
Playing at bagammon,
Swim for divarsion
  All round this hulk ;
There ' Saxon' sailors
Keep brave repailers,
Who soon with sailors
  Must anchor weigh
From th' Em'rald Island,
Ne'er to see dry land
Until they spy land
  In sweet Bot'ny Bay.

EXTRACTS

From the Writings of Mr. R. A. Wilson,

BARNEY MAGLONE,

Formerly Editor of the "Enniskillen Advertiser."

The Bard of the Poor.

(Written for the Burns Centenary Poems in 1859.)

Fill high to the conqueror's name !
  He hath triumphed o'er narrow-souled wrong,
Till he stands on the ever-bright summit of fame,
  The low-born monarch of song.
Praise the " Voice of Coila" aloud,
  And forget the dark shame of the past,
That he, of whom nations are proud to be proud,
  Got the grave of a gauger at last !
Then send round the cup to the name of the dead,
And forget how the living was furnished with bread !

In *his* day how patronage ran,
  'Mong the high-born, wealthy, and wise ;
God made him an orator, poet. and MAN—
  THEY made him a hound of Excise !
'Tis past ; and, at Fashion's command,
  The soft tide of flattery turns,
Till the highest and haughtiest heads in the land
  Are bowed to the genius of Burns.
Then his dust to the dust ; and his soul to its rest ;
But his mem'ry to those who can cherish it best !

The mem'ry of Burns, it is ours—
  The people's—for he was our own ;
The flash of his spirit, the sweep of his powers,
  Went forth for the people alone.
He sang of our hopes and our fears ;
  He pictured our sorrow and wrongs ;
The love of our hearts, and the salt of our tears,
  Were the rich reaming cream of his songs.
And we claim, as our right, and our pride evermore.
The mem'ry of Burns, the Bard of the Poor.

To countries unknown when he died
  The people have carried his fame ;
The far Xarra Yarra, and Oregon's tide,
  Like the Doon, or the Ayr, know his name,
In the lands where the hot brow is fanned,
  By the spice-laden wing of the breeze,
On the bison-swept plains of the Western land,
  In the isles of the summery seas,—
The people exult in the Doon's noble swan,
The high-hearted, out-spoken champion of Man !

And ours be the task to proclaim,
    And cherish his name to the end ;
Our love shall with jealousy watch o'er the fame
    Of our poet—our brother—our friend.
In the midst of our cares and our pains,
    When the soul is with troubles o'ercast,
In the holy of holies within us remains
    A green little spot to the last ;
And there in soul sunshine, shall bloom evermore.
The mem'ry of Burns, the BARD OF THE POOR !

On the margin of the Book, containing a collection of competition Poems, published for the Centenary of Robert Burns, the following appears in the author's handwriting :—

The writer of this piece *refused* to engage in any competition ; but sent those Stanzas to Mr. Finlay, of the *Northern Whig,* with a request that if thought worthy they should be published with the competition poems. Mr. Finlay wrote to Mr. Wilson that if he had complied with the terms, it would have been deemed the best of the Belfast pieces. The Messrs. Murray, of Glasgow, when writing to Mr. Wilson for leave to put the poem into their book, expound themselves in the same way. Mr Wilson's object in sending in writing the thing at all, was to express the Democratic feeling which claims Burns as its own, in *defiance* of the fashionable pretences that made the enemies ot Burns' sentiments get up a demonstration to his memory. That was why this piece was offered in *opposition* to the rules.

Our Own Fireside.

May you never know a sorrow,
    May you never feel a fear,
And may disappointment shun you,
    In the coming happy year.
May all trouble fly your presence,
    And all peace with you abide,
Through a happy, happy year,
    At your own fireside—
        In the town, upon the hill,
          By the river's rolling tide,
        May the smiles of love be round you,
          At your own fireside.

May the brow of age be placid,
    May the heart of youth be light ;
May the feeble limbs be strengthened.
    And the sickly eyes grow bright ;
May the loving looks of gladness
    Flash around you far and wide,
And the centre of all pleasure
    Be your own fireside—
        Yes, your own fireside—
          Yes, your bright fireside—
        Through a happy, happy year
          At your own fireside.

Bernardo's Revenge.

A SEQUEL TO MRS HEMAN'S "SPANISH CHAMPION."

What tents glem, on the green hill's side, like snow in the sun's young beam ?
Whose gloomy warriors gather there, like a surly mountain stream ?
These are Bernardo's warriors ; they come, like a stormy blast,
The dark red rage of their cherished hate on the cruel king to cast.
Their chief, like a spirit of vengeance, now, is urging on his men—
Woe ! woe to the king, if he meet that look—he'll ne'er see man again !
" Haters of tyranny," cries the chief, " see yonder slavish host ;
You must drench the field with their craven blood or freedom's hopes are lost
You know that I come, for a father's death, the debt of hate to pay ;
Then let the " murdered Sancho," be your battle cry to-day
Now on for the death, of the tyrant king !" " Hurrah" was the answering cry,
" We follow you to victory ; or we follow you to die !"
Hurrah for the death of the tyrant king ! his treacherous reign is o'er,
We'll crush the viper brood to-day ; or breathe heaven's air no more.
Let's change the scene.   The battle field is full before us now ;
The rout ! the shout ! the lightning flash of Bernardo's angry brow.
" Oh, brave avengers, on " he cries, " the foe gives way—come on !"
His cries are mixed with the victors' shout, and the vanquished's dying groan
The chieftain's arm is weary now ; his hacked hand drips with gore,
But one last sacrifice remains before his toil is o'er.
The king, who looked for victory from his large and well trained host,
But full before, with blood red sword, a warrior appears ;
And the war-cry, " Murdered Sancho," rings in the tyrant's ears.
" Ha, noble king, have I met you here !" with scornful smile he cries—
" Don Sancho's son must talk with you once more before he dies
Your kindness to my sainted sire is graven on my heart,
And I must show my gratitude, Sir King, before we part.
Draw, for the last of Sancho's race is ready for your sword ;
Bernardo's blood should flow by him by whom his sires was poured.
What wait you for, vile craven wretch ? It was not thus you stood
While laying out your fiendish plans to shed my father's blood !
Draw, sir, before I learn from you th' assassin's coward trade,
And write the lessons that you teach, upon your perjured head !"
Roused by the storm of fiery taunts the King at length engaged—
He fought for life ; but all in vain th' unequal strife waged :
Bernardo's falchion pierced his breast, the warm blood spouted o'er
The reeking blade, he groaning fell—Alphonso is no more !
The warrior kneels on the still warm corpse, and looking up he cries,
" Spirit of murdered Sancho, look on this last sacrifice !"
Then rising, cries " Ho ! stop the fight, the tyrant's reign is o'er
My keen sword had fulfilled my vow and thirsts for blood no more."

Let Erin Remember.

Let Erin remember the days gone by,
    And mingle her joy with sadness
For the time when her hymn was a party cry,
    And the heart beat with party madness—
When her sons fierce words of defiance hurled,
    And the weapons of murder handled
Let her ne'er forget how the pitying world
    By her conduct then was scandaled.

Dialogue between 12th July and St. Patrick's Day.

July the first, one morning clear,
   Met Patrick's Day out walkin';
They nodded dhry enough at first,
   An' then dhropped into talkin'

Says brisk July, " Bedad it's dry
   This way we have of greetin';
This glow'r and bob we give, by gob.
   Is not like naybors meetin'!

I don't see why culd times gone by
   Need make us meet so shyly :
Now, is it, Pat, a rayson that
   We'd pass each other dhrylry ?,

If at the Boyne your frens and mine.
   Stood up for James and Willy,
For us to scould er look so cowld
   About it's mortal silly.

If they were right, they had their fight,
   And so it should be ended ;
If they were wrong, its far too long
   Ago for us to mend it."

Says Patrick's Day, "That's jist the way
   A naybor should be talkin';
So here's my hand, my dacent man ;
   Let's chat a bit while walking.

If you must walk, and dhrum and talk,
   I't useless to be mulish.
Sure I can do the same thing too,
   An' be as wise—or foolish.

Our fathers fought when both sides thought
   'Twas Ireland's cause they stood for
But you an' I, I think, might thry
   What unity is good for."

July and Pat thus had their chat,
   While dandhrin' on like naybors ;
An' as for those who'd make them foes,
   Bad luck attend their labors.

Coortin'.

Och blissins on the frosty night,
   An' blessins on the win'.
An' blissins on the dhriftin' snow
   That keeps the people in—

That keeps them at the fireside,
   Or in the corner dark,
To do what Yankee damsels do
   When they begin to " spark."

The win' might blow its light to chaff
   The sky come down in snow,
If I were in the corner snng,
   With somebody I know.

The storm might roar creation deaf,
   The night might freeze *go bragh*,
If I could make that somebody's
   Wee heart begin to thaw.

On a New Invention called a Bonnet.

Jist let me mention
That quare invention
Of small extension
　　Above the brow—
Had I a sonnet
I'd sing it on it
That powltice bonnet
　　They're wearin' now.
Och, surely this is
Conthrived for kisses,
The balmy blisses
　　A lover sips;
The dhroll wee threzhure
Just fits the plezhure
When fond ones mezhure
　　Two pair of lips.

No brim cocks over
To pleague the lover,
There's not a cover
　　On brow or hair;
'Twas surely Vaynius
That had the jaynius
To plan these haynius
　　Wee things they ware.
Were I Layandher.
That sallymandher
That could mayandher
　　Through waves an' wind.
I'd sing these wilers,
These angel smilers,
These heart-beguilers
　　Called womankind.

A Merry Conceit.

I sing of the land, the merry merry land,
Where the churchyard rat is feeding
So dainty, on the cold cold corpse,
And the blood filled worm is breeding
In the breast or the brain of the buried one,
And building its nest so neatly
In the heart's deep core of the quiet quiet corpse
And drinking its blood so sweetly !
The grave ! the grave !! the deep dark grave !!!
What house upon earth is so pleasant !
Where the fear falls not, where the heart sighs not,
Where the king's but a match for the peasant.
Where the poor man's ears are free from the din
Of his wife's or his children's bawling.
But he lies so snug—ha ! ha ! how snug !
And the worms thro' and thro' him crawling !
Oh who wouldn't live in the calm cold grave,
With a blanket of worms around him,
And the rats, in their glee, laughing heartily
At the thought of their having found him,
No rent is paid for the narrow old house ;
'Tis a cheap and a quiet lodging ;
And there's no canny trick in old death's estate,
The tenant his landlord dodging !

On an Infant's Death.

Thou hast gone pretty bud
　　To the garden of God,
To bloom in the bowers of bliss—
　　To the unclouded home
Where the storms never come,
That threatened to blight thee in
　　this.

Though hast left me to weep
　　O'er the place of thy sleep,
Where the rank nettle waves o'er thy
　　head,
　　But 'tis all for the best,
　　Since the soul is at rest,
Then, why should my tears be shed ?

To the Man who Prents the Darry Jurnal.

Sir,—As you know the feelins I enthertain for Mr. Maglone, will you plaze send him the enclosed letther, and tell him that altho I am makin him an offer of marridge, it's not for want of plenty of sweetharts of me own here, for I've more nor fifty of them, an' one of them was up in the balloon with himself, an more than that, staid longer in it an was hire up.—Your sarvint,

Shuzy Sharples.

TO MISTER MAGLONE, PUDDIN LANE, ENNISKILLEN.

Shugarhouse-lane, Darry, January, 1868

Dear Barney—I hope you'll not think it surprisin'
To be hearin from one that you never set eyes on ;
But I'm ever an' always your letthers purusin'
An' find them so droll an' so mity amusin',
At times so poetick, at all times so witty,
An' sumtimes so sad, that, from first feelin' pity,
I'm head over ears in love with you grown,
An' cant help addressin' you, Barney Maglone.

I first felt the pity. dear Barney, aroon,
The time you fell down from the great big balloon ;
But tho' I felt sorry, I wont tell a fib,
I was glad that you then couldn't call me a rib ;
For I'm told that all those you had at the time
Got a crush that had near put an end to your rhyme.
Och, the heart of the girl was as hard as a stone
That didn't feel sorry then, Barney Maglone.

You say you are lonely, an' I know from your tune
Yourself is the dog that complained to the moon
But why are you lonely ? when all you've to do
Is to seek out some heart that'll always be true.
I've a long time to go till I'll be on the shelf,
An' as this is a lep yer, I'd ask you meself
If I only just thought you would call me your own,
An' throw up Almantha, dear Barney Maglone.

It's all very fine, and I dar say romantic,
To be dyin' for one that's across the Atlantic ;
But birds have fine feathers when far, far away,
An' I'm sartin she's not half as nice as you say.
But whether or not shure it's all one to me,
If you think, Barney darlin', that we could agree ;
You'd find in a short time you'd alther your tone,
With me to console you, dear Barney Maglone.

You're fond of black hair—mine's as black as a raven,
An' tho' I'm not rich you'll find I am savin'.
Me complexshun is good, tho' inclined to be florid,
An' I've what you would call an intelligent forrid.
If it's coortin' you want, troth you'll get it galore!
I'll kiss you an' coax you, an' fifty things more,
That 'll make you regret you've been so long alone ;
Now, what do you think of that, Barney Maglone?

So Barney, avic, if you only are willin',
I'll vex all the girls about Enniskillen;
I don't care a straw for the lashins of mud in
The town. for my *shugar* will sweeten my puddin'.
So write to me, darli', an' just let me know
What day you would like me to pack up and go.
I'd be prouder by far than the Queen on her throne,
If you'd only address me as Mrs. Maglone.

I wanted to asner the exygetical Shuzy in orthodocks methre ; but I was
fear'd to go to the masther of the Muddle School, or the newspaper chap, to
rightify it for me ; for I didn't want them to know that a bashful modest
crather like me, that never yet had impedince enough to stan up for my own,
would have curage to write a love-letther, barrin to you. So I had to thry it
myself this way—

Och, Shuzy, *would* you come to me ?
  Or are you only jokin?
You've dhrawn the heart up to my throte,
  Till, dad, I'm fairly chokin!
It bothers me to dhraw my breth,
  The way I'm palpytatin ;
It's what my left han ribs are sore,
  My heart has *sich* a batin.

Och, *Wuirre*! haisge! Shuzy dear!
  Would you be raly willin
To come "from Derry walls away,"
  An' live in Enniskillen?
To lave the lordly banks of Foyle,
  The Maiden City's glory,
An' seek the bow'ry isles of Erne—
  Mavrone! I doubt the story!

Is may be thrue ; but och, I fear
  It's nothin more than blarney—
What! lave your "Meg" and "Prentice Boys"
  For Puddin-lane an' Barney!
But if you mane it. *sho mo lamh!*
  My heart's half yours already ;
An' when you have it all your own,
  You'll find it brave an' steady.

I'll love you as the ivy loves
  The oak to which it's clingin;
Or as the sprick'ld throut the burn
  That wandher's o'er it singin;
Or as the levrock loves the air,
  Or mackeral the oshan ;
Or as the bendin sun-flow'r loves
  The lord of her devotion.

I got that about the sun-flower from your cunthry, Almantha. But I
had to drop the rhymin, seein I wasn't able to give as good as I got. How-
anever, I must thrinnle myself down to Derry some day soon, an' thry the
taste of Shugar-house lane, instead of waitin for Tom's ould shoes, or livin any
longer in a purgathry of buttons, an' collars, an' parboil'd xistence. The
Journal man or Mr. Frank O'Neill 'll be able to tell me where Shuzy lives ; an'
if *she* fits an' *I* fit, they may shut up all the coortin-shops in Derry ; for kissin
ill be chape.

THE IRISH CRY.

There's a wail from the glen; there's a groan from the hill;
'Tis the cry of the land 'gainst the Fiend of the Still!
'Tis the *caoine* of Erin—the *caoine* so dread
That swells for the living, and not for the dead—
The living! the smitten—the blasted—the seared—
The souls by the slime of the drink-snake besmeared.
From the home on the upland, the hut in the dale,
From hamlet and city, is bursting the wail.
'Tis the sob of the wife; 'tis the moan of the child;
'Tis the groan of a nation by bloodshed defiled.
From the heart of the orphan it pierces the air;
It bursts from the widow's white lips of despair;
It moans from the roofles, untenanted walls;
And, gurgling and choked, from the gallows it falls!
It sobs o'er the grave where the drinker is laid;
It shrieks from the soul of the maiden betrayed;
It bursts from the poor-house, the mad-house, the gaol;
This woeful—despairing—wide—wild Irish wail!
Up! Children of Erin, respond to the cry!
For man's sake—for God's sake—up! *act* in reply!
For the sake of the soul-smitten slave of the cup—
For the sake of *his* victims—up! countrymen, up!
By the hell in his heart, and the hell that he fears;
By his wife and his children—their torture and tears—
Up! act! nor be backward with heart, voice, or hand,
Till the King-fiend of curses is swept from our land.
Heave up the old land into daylight again,
The smiled on by Heaven—a praise among men.
Wring the curse from her heart, wipe the stain from her sod;
Roll her out among nations an island of God!

TO ——

Seen no more, forgotten never—thou whose image must for ever
O'er my life-path cast a shadow of commingled bliss and pain—
Shadow of a visioned rapture that my spirit saw in vain;—
Would that I had never met thee! would that I could now forget thee!
Since no changing fate can set thee as my lone life-star again—
Since my dreary heart is destined in its darkness to remain.

Thou wert as a fountain springing—laughing—flashing—sparkling—singing—
In the dreary soul-Sahara where my spirit gasping stands,
And in vain one drop of coolness for its torturing thirst demands,
As I stooped to drink, it vanished—from my burning lips was banished—
In the treeless arid desert swallowed by the thirsty sands—
Sands that form the red sepulchres of the simoom-blasted bands.

Could I but again behold thee! could I only once enfold thee
To this hunger-wasted bosom that is famishing for thee
Like a doom'd and dying sailor tossed upon a sail-less sea.
But—no matter—all is ended. Perished is the hope that blended
With my wild rapt dreams, so splendid—ended evermore for me.
Dark-eyed haunter of my spirit, let me dream no more of thee.

Here on earth asunder driven, parted as the poles of heaven,
Sever'd like the thunder-riven fragments of the blasted oak,
Dashed upon the earth and shattered by the fated lightning stroke,—
Never more—oh, never—never is there aught that can deliver
From the deathy drear sensation with which dreaming hope awoke,
When the lurid light of real life upon my spirit broke.

I must tame these wild sensations; I must hide these pained pulsations;
Nor give token of the torture that in silence preys on me,
Like Alcides' fabled garment in its burning agony.
All I ask is, let me never dream again, but careless ever
On life's swiftly-rushing river float into eternity
There, upon the shoreless ocean, I shall claim my right in thee.

Hearts that this vile world has blighted, souls that in this world are slighted,
Shall in the Unseen be righted—righting all that's here amiss.
In *that* world shall be united severed hearts that bleed in *this*
There the souls that earth has riven to each other shall be given,
Each to each a wond'rous heaven of unspoken speechless bliss—
Each shall there find in the other's love a fathomless abyss.

Where no earthly whim divideth, where the mystic soul-bark glideth
'Mong the stellar isles of glory that bedeck duration's sea,
Thou, on earth adored so vainly, thou shalt float along with me.
On that voyage never ending, our two souls for ever blending,
To eternal oneness tending, I shall sail along with thee,
Bright and beauteous, rare and radiant hope of my eternity.

A STREET BALLAD.

The cow that lived in Armagh was sent to forrin parts,
An' lavin' of her family it nearly broke their hearts;
The mother an' the sisther, likewise the poor wee calf,
All sobb'd an' roared like murdher—in throth, you needn't laugh.
" Och, darlin'," says the ould cow, " I'll never see you more;
They're dhrivin' you to Belfast, that dismal place, asthore;
They'll tie you up an' feed you, an' milk you in a house —
As long as you're among them, they'll niver let you lowse;
For in that barb'rous cunthry you'll lade a dismal life,
Till at the last, acushla, you get the butcher's knife!
Och, fare-you-well for iver, my darlin' an' my pride,
I'll never see you grazin' in buty by my side!"
She got a fourth-class ticket, an' stharted from the town,
An' slither'd on the railroad along by Portadown,
By Lurgan an' by Moira, an' Lisburn, till at last
The exile landed safely in sorrow in Belfast.
But weary on the wether, an' weary on the town;
Like pourin out of dishes the rain was tumblin' down,
The sthreets were flat an' muddy, the rain lay on them deep,
The Poun' Burn too was rowlin' across them with a sweep,
The poor forlorn sthranger she knew not what to do,
Not bein' a town counsellor or peeler, wirresthrue !
She wander'd in the wather—still deeper—bliss'd day !
Till at the last it swep' her, poor crathur, clane away.
'Twould break your heart to see her when strugglin' in the tide,

The muddy wather washin' again' her sleekit side.
Her kickin' all was useless, her moanin' was in vain;
She'll niver bite a daisy, or chew her cud agric.
With bubblin' moans she mutther'd with her last bit of breath,
" Upon the Corporation I lay my guilty death.
Let all young cows take warnin' from me, and stay at home .
An' niver be persuaded to sich a place to roam.
Belfast sthreets were invented for dhrownin cows I know."
Her head sank in the water, and ended all her woe.
No more along the loanin' when comin' home she'll low,
She'll never kick her heels with joy to meet a neighbour cow.
In vain for her grow shamrocks, the fields are green in vain,
She'll niver lay her sleek side along the grass again.
A curse is on the flat sthreets an' on the muddy tide,
Where in her pride and beauty the innocent cow died.

FILLAN O'CARROLL,

A Legend of Ballycastle.

WHERE lone Dunaneeny's sad ruins are looming
O'er the sea-hallowed caves in which dark waves are booming;
Where Caenbaan's pallid brow meets the storm-winds of heaven,
When the rage of the North o'er the ocean is driven,
While the shriek of the gull and the storm-spirit's yelling
On the mist and the spray of the sea-blast are swelling—
Lived Fillan O'Carroll : a name known to glory
Ere Erin of Songs gave her sadness to story—.
Ere the sun of her pride from her sky had departed—
Ere she felt the deep sting of the treacherous-hearted—
Ere the neck of the vanquished bowed down to the stronger
And Erin of Swords was a nation no longer.

He lived in a time when to live was to battle,
When the wild joy of life was the war-tempest's rattle.
He was fierce, like his age, as the storm of the mountain,
His honour was pure as the rock-born fountain ;
In his red hour of anger no being was wilder,
In his calm day of kindness no mortal was milder.
Though his course in the field was o'er smitten and dying,
And his sword's lightning flashed in the path of the flying,
When Victory's sun chased the darkness of danger
His heart and his hall both belonged to the stranger.

But, though beloved by the youthful and hoary,
Though bards lit their songs with the gleams of his glory,
Though no one might risk with him combat or quarrel,—
A cloud darkly set on the soul of O'Carroll.
For him were high bosoms with deep longings laden,
His name shook the rose on the cheek of the maiden,
Sweet lips breathed it softly in solitude lying,
But vainly the daughters of Uladh were sighing.
He loved. But no daughter of Erin had bound him
With her spell-weaving eyes, flinging wildly around him

The chains of bright beauty. No earth-born creature,
With grace in each movement and bliss in each feature,
Had made him her captive. His heart's deep devotion
Went forth to a mystical ribh of the ocean.
When the moon from o'er Margy, so solemnly tender,
Shone down on Ceanbaan with her softness of splendour—

One night, when the bay in that radiance lay sleeping,
The child of the billow a vigil was keeping
On a ripple kissed rock where the wave's gentle motion
Seemed whisp'ring to earth a love-tale from the ocean.
In beauty unearthly, ineffably splendid,
Her whispers of song with the low ripples blendid,
The chief saw and heard. From that moment enchanted,
By her look and her voice he was day and night haunted.
When the wrath of the storm round his ramparts was ringing,
He heard the strange voice of the sea-maiden singing ;
When the smile of the sky on the calm sea was gleaming,
He saw her long locks on the lazy wave streaming ;—
And while he bent over—his hands fiercely clasping,
His face wildly pale and his proud bosom gasping,
From those locks' floating glory a smile would come stealing
That filled him with rapturous faintness of feeling.

No more for O'Carroll the soft clairseach sounded ;
No more for O'Carroll the fierce war-steed bounded ;
His thoughts were no more of the warriors' anger,
The breaking of spears or the shields' clashing clangour.
O'er the wind-beaten, spray-swept Ceantaan he strayed lonely,
His thought of the weird one—his thought of her only.
One day as he bent o'er the wave in his sadness,
With thoughts surging through him that wrought him to madness,
The mystical being arose in her splendour,
And sang in strange notes words enthrallingly tender :—

THE SEA MAIDEN'S SONG.

Child of earth, with the brow of sadness,
    Come from a world where anguish reigns ;
Come to the deep blue halls of gladness
    That open for thee in our wide domains.

Treasures so vast that thy wildest dreaming
    Never hath pictured them, shall be thine ;
Thy path shall be lit by the diamond's gleaming,
    Round thee a world of gems shall shine.

An immortal bosom shall be thy pillow,
    Unwithering lips shall press thy brow ;
No son of the earth, no child of the billow,
    Hath been, or shall be, loved as thou.

A heart shall be thine whose faintest feeling
    Would form the soul of a child of earth,
And the fire of my lips through thy life-tide stealing
    Shall change the blood of thy grosser birth.

Come ! as thou passest the wondrous portal
    That leads away to my radiant home,
That death-doomed form shall become immortal ;
    Heir of mortality, come—oh, come !

Come with me to where Death shall never
  His dark'ning shadow fling o'er thy brow ;
Where Love and Rapture are young for ever—
  Child of sadness come with me now !

Deep into-his spirit she gazed as she ended ;
The words of her song with that spirit's thoughts blended ;
He plunged from the rock, and the eddying water
Closed over the chief and the billow's bright daugrter.
He died—*did* he die ? The old legend deposes
That far in the depth of the ocean reposes
(With a high-heaving sky of blue billows to cover)
The maid of the deep with her earth-born lover.

New worlds have been found, and old nations have perished,
Since Fillan was first in his ocean-home cherished.
Though age after age hath passed silently o'er him,
Though ages have passed since Earth ceased to deplore him,
He loves as he loved—as he must love for ever :
Time's lapse hath no power these two souls to sever ;
For their hearts and their beings are doomed to be blended,
Till the Archangel's fiat on Time hath descended.

But the legend relates that should Erin's sons ever
Unite like one soul in some holy endeavour
To raise their sunk land from her posture so lowly,
And save her with effort and enterprise holy,—
To bless them—to aid them—to crown their devotion,
The sea-lady's spouse shall come back from the ocean.
Should the sun ever see Erin's sons without quarrel,
Green Ulster again shall see Fillan O'Carroll.

[Dunaneeny is an old ruin on the cliff to the north-west of Ballycastle Quay.
  Ceanbaan means Fairhead. It is the cliff to the west of Ballycastle Bay, and
is white : but, by some profound exercise of cockney geography, or hydro-
graphy, the name, in its English form is given to Benmore, on the east side,
which is a dark head. *Ribh*, or *Rib*, means a syren, mermaid, or some such
being, who used to live and sing in the days of good neighbours, but who
seems incapable of mingling in society during the reign of crinoline and
political expediency.]

A POTHEEN BALLAD.

My fren Mr. Fox is as good a han' at makin' the English fly roun' him as you'd see in a small distance an' a half. It was put on him one time that he couldn't make a song like the love-ballads that be a singin' on the sthreet. " Done," says Mickey; " you'll see an' hear tell if I don't" So a dale of time didn't get lave to slip roun' till he had this spun on the ould woollen wheel of his jaynius—

Ot all the navvygations
  That ever left the shore,
I tell this mortal nation,
  It's potheen I adore.

I love the tendher crather
  All in her punchy dhress,
An' when she's mother-naked
  I love her none the less.

If she had but a night-dhress
  Of shuggar on her skin,
I'm not the boy that would refuse
  To take the swate one in.

Well I mind the lively night
  Her mother, Still, lay in ;
Often did I press the babe
  Between my nose an' chin ;

An', if she was as ould as
  Methoosalem's first hat,
I'd love her as the crame's lov'd by
  That sleekit baste, the cat.

If mighty Dutheronmy,
  That hayro of renown,
Likewise July-us Saizer
  That won the British crown—

If valyant Demmygorgon,
  Pittollomy an' Pan,
Along with bould Kallipso
  That own'd the Isle of Man—

If Heethor an' bould Vaynus,
  With Lu-sy-an the ass,
Also Neb-you-codnayzer,
  So mighty at the grass—

Were all with Martin Luther,
  With Gladstone an' brave Lowe,—
I'd box them right and left afore
  I'd let my charmer go.

I's thrue she has been thricky,
  As Irish maids do be ;
An' I must own that sometimes
  She's play'd a prank on me.

The rowl'd me in the soft mud,
  One night she got me down,
When I was just meeandhrin'
  About a mile from town.

She gave my eyes a paintin',
  An' gave my nose a swell,
Another winther's evenin'
  When huggin' her too well.

But all these lovin' capers
  I aisily forgive ;
An' if she knocks my branes out
  I'll love her while I live.

I'd face the French and Prooshans
  An' the Permissive Bill,
Afore I'd lose my darlin',
  The daughter ot the still.

TO A YOUNG LADY FOR HER CARTE-DE-VISITE ALBUM.

Fill it up with kindly faces—
  Those on which you love to gaze ;
Those on which you eyes may linger
  Sadly-fond in future days.

When life's present ties are broken—
  When the world hath scattered wide
Those you now love, lady, let them
  In these pages still abide.

When the cherished ones have perished
  ' Dust to Dust' been o'er them said,
Let their dear lamented features
  In these pages still be read.

Every page shall then be sweetly
  Sanctified as friendship's shrine :
And amid these faces, lady,
  Let me beg a place for mine.

THE "DEVENISH'S" FAREWELL.

Farewell to Peggy Elliott,
  My first love and my last!
How sweet 'twas to behould her
  At Thrasna, as I passed.
Och, never more she'll meet me,
  As I slip o'er the wave;
Och, never more she'll greet me,
  With orange flags so brave.
Her music may be silent,
  Her flags may wave no more;
For I'll be far from Peggy
  An' Thrasna's lovely shore!
Farewell to my own island,
  With all its ould remains—
Its tower so gray an' lofty
  That bothers all their brains!
It's it that is the wondher,
  So plain an' so sublime,
The lofty sphinx of Erin,
  The riddle of ould Time;
For, since the noble Danaans
  Were driven from the land,
It's jist a mason wondher,
  So simple an' so grand.
It may have stood in Dev'nish
  When Pharoah had the gout;
Maybe when Ceadir-lamh-hor
  From Sodom got the rout.
It may have been, whèn David
  Sung sweet on Zion's hill,
That this ould tower of Dev'nish
  Was where we see it still.
It may have been, when Cæsar
  From Brutus got the prod,
That this same tower was standin'
  Upon this same green sod.
While many a lofty nation
  Has risen an' decay'd,
The tower stands as stately
  As when it first was made.
The sthrame of Time has passed it
  An' left it as it stood,
While Greece, an' Roome, an' Aigypt,
  Have parished in the flood.
An' maybe 'twill be standin'
  When Greece is great again,
An' when the Moorish standards
  Are floatin' over Spain.
When on the Guadalquiver
  Refinement reigns once more,
The tower may still be standin'
  Upon this pleasant shore.
When Britain is forgotten,
  When Erin reigns again,

An' Judah is a nation,
  The tower may still remain,
But I will ne'er behould it;
  I'm off to black Belfast,
To see if Thomas Devlin
  Can save me at the last!

Farewell to Enniskillen,
  To sweet Loch Erne's shore,
An' all the leafy islands
  That I must see no more.
Farewell to Joseph Lingard—
  To my beloved Patt Hall,
Who wrought for me and cared me,
  An' stuck to me through all—
To Carson, Kittson, Armstrong—
  To manly sow'ld George Black!
Ochone, but it was cheerin'
  While he was at my back!
An' as for Mr. Porther,
  My father an' my friend,
May all success attend him,
  An' glory without end.
An', och! farewell forever,
  Ye fairies of the land
That us'd upon my deck to dance
  Or on my bridge to stand.
No more your lovely faces
  Shall o'er my bulwark peep
An' in Loch Erne's wathers
  See angels in the deep.
The sunny eyes from Cavan,
  The smiles from Lisnaskea,
The charms of Enniskillen,
  Have pass'd from me away.
Farewell to Dr. Bagot
  An' also Torney Graham—
To Derrygore's sweet cottage
  An' to Portora sthrame.
Farewell to all the places
  I ne'er shall see again—
The brick-yard and the market,
  Dear dirty School-house Lane,
The homely wharf, the workhouse,
  The purty Piper's Isle,
An' the green fields of George Willis
  That used on me to smile,
The barrack an' Portora,
  The isle whose name I bear—
If fortune had but ordher'd
  That I'd be shipwreck'd there,
Instead of bein' banish'd
  From all so dear an' fair!
O wirresthruc, glan waideen,

But this is hard to bear!
Farewell, ye sparklin' wathers
  That us'd to kiss my bow ;
The thick mud of the Lagan
  Must be my shilter now,
Unless the corporation
  Keep up the same ould rate—
Then High-sthreet an' North-sthreet
  I'll proudly navvygate.

Farewell to the Bow Island,
- To Castlecallwell's shades,
To slopin' Magh'rameena
  With all its dancin' maids.
Farewell, ye mazy islands,
  So thickly green an' fair,
I lave my heart among you—
  I lave you in despair.

THE LOST EMIGRANTS.

Down in the deep sad sea
  That moaneth evermore.
Beneath the wave that pours it's wail
  Upon a foreign shore,

They lie—they young, the beautiful,
  The hoping and the brave—
Far from the green churchyards at
    home,
  In an unhallowed grave.

No mourning face bends over them ;
  No tears of love are shed
Above the spot where heaves the deep
  O'er the uncoffined dead

Alas ! the lost ones left with hope
  That, in the years to come,
Their steps returning yet would tread
  The dear old spots at home—

The shamrock'd slope, the daisied
    brae,
  The mountain side and glen—
That they would make the old roof
    ring
  With merriment again.

'Twas vain : no mother's kiss of love,
  No father's trembling hand,
Shall welcome back the wanderer
  To love and native land.

The home may be as homely still,
  The fields be still as green ;
But not to Christ returns to earth
  Shall they again be seen.

Oh misery ! that such a land
  Must send her sons abroad
To seek the life they cannot find
  Upon the natal sod.

Our Father, God, reverse the doom
  That forces us to roam ;
And speed the day when Irishmen
  Shall find a home at home !

The EMIGRANT'S RETURN

River, river, rippling river,
  Dancing down to the summer sea,
Beauty beaming from thy bosom,
  Sunshine shimm'ring upon thee,—

When I dream of thy winding waters
  Bathing banks that are bright with
    flowers,
Sad sweet mem'ries, o'er me stealing,
  Bear me back to my boyhood's
    hours.

Would I were where thy bright wave-
    lets
  Wand'ring to the sea are seen,
From Glenshesk and dark-dun Carey,
  By the banks of Lag-a-leen.

Lag-a-leen, thy banks of of alder,
  Bushy hollows, grassy braes,
Pebbly marge and rippling Margy,
  All bring back my boyhood's days—

Those bright days of young wild
    wonder,
  When to live was but a dream.
As my childhood musing wander'd
  By thy legend-haunted stream.

Soon, O rippling, murm'ring Margy,
  Shalt thou as in old time flow,
While the head now thinking of thee
  In the dust is lying low.

Other steps with thee shall wander,
  Other eyes gaze on thy stream,
When this heart and brain no longer
  Can of care or rapture dream.

In dear Erin's fairer future,
  Other tongues shall sing of thee,
When some namless grass-roofed
    dwelling
  Holds the dust that now is me.

Rippling river, rapturous river,
  Blessed be thy banks for aye,
When oblivion's stream hath carried
  This poor musing waif away.

THE DUEL.

Ye sprites who preside over heroic song,
Let your sowl-thrilling fire thro' my veins shoot along,
While I sing how Ould Sulky, the gallant and strong,
    Has doctor'd the doctor this morning.

The squabble respected the right to a pass
Through a field where Don Medico gather'd his grass,
But who was the wise one, and who was the ass,
    Is a touch above Barney this morning.

Ould Sulky and Creden were ranged on one side,
On the other two doctors stood up in their pride;
And the river stood still to see what would betide
    Between printing and pills in the morning.

"Now, Ball," says Mahood, "show your medical pluck;
Take courge ould sort, an' you'll maybe have luck.
Holy Nelly! you look like a pig that was stuck,
    You're so pale round the gills in the morning."

Says Creden, "Now, Sulky, take care what you're at!
Give another cock-up to the gallant ould hat;
Keep cool as an oyster—you'll nab him that's flat—
    He'll croak on the meadow this morning!"

The distance was measured, the pistols all right
All chivalrous measures arranged for the fight,
And each gallant combatant held his breath tight—
    Bent on glory or death in the morning.

At the shot the bould doctor fell down like a sack,
Or like Richard the Third when he flops on his back.
"Och Mahood," says he, "did you hear that crack?
    Dar a Muire I'm murdher'd this morning."

Oh woe to the county, and woe to the town!
The pride of our doctors is now smitten down!
Sulky's curs'd leadin' article's set in his crown—
    No skill can avail him this morning.

The crowd gather'd round at the horrible sight
Of the gallant young doctor laid low in such plight,
And two or three fainted clean dead with the fright
    And had to be doctor'd this morning.

But, joy to the town, he was not dead at all,
But only dumfounder'd a bit by the fall;
The county still prides in her own gallant Ball,
    He's living and kicking this morning.

Says Dr. Mahood, "Take him home to his bed;
He's nothing the worse of a ball in the head;
It's only a little more lead to his lead—
    He's as safe as salt herrings this morning."

Now glory and honor for ever befall
The gallant cocked hat and the sturdy owl shawl,
And all sorts of credit attend Dr. Ball—
    For their deeds of renown wrought this morning.

If an army of devils, led on by old Nick,
Should land in our country, we'd play them a trick;
For Sulky himself the invaders could lick—
    Aye, before breakfast-time in the morning !

THE WESTERN IRELAND.

I must carry you now to strange bright scenes,
    And to places far away,
Whence many a sad fond thought looks back
    To the green old hills to-day—
To the daisied fields, to the shamrock'd slopes,
    To the streams and hazel dells,
To the lowly, cozy, dear thatched cots,
    Where many a loved one dwells.

I must carry you hence to proud New York,
    And its bay of the winding shore—
To the cloudy spray that is shaken by
    Niagara's ceaseless roar—
To the river that feeds the cataract,
    To Ontario's inland sea,
And the lordly sweep of St. Lawrence wave,
    You must come to-night with me.

The Summer scene, and the Winter scene,
    And many an Autumn hue
Of the grand, mysterious Western land,
    Shall be viewed to-night by you :
And the sunny South, where the shackled slave
    Bows down to the lash no more ;
Where the chain is broken, the whip consumed,
    And slavery's reign is o'er.

And in all these places our kith and kin
    Are seeking for their rest,
The Pilgrims of Hope in every land,
    But chiefly in the West.
More of our kindred are dwelling there
    Than here on the green sod stand ;
So the country we show you to-night
    Is the western Ireland.

KING DEATH.

Let's sing of the land, the merry,
    merry land,
  Where the church-yard rat is feed-
    ing
So daintily on the quiet, quiet corpse,
  And the blood-gorged worm is
    breeding
In the heart or the brain of the buried
    one,
  Or building its nest so neatly
In the poor old holes that once were
    eyes,
  And filling them up completely!

What jolly, jolly fun when the clay
    comes down,
  The clods on the black lid falling,
When the fat old rats are poking
    around,
  And the lazy worms are crawling !
There's true tenant-right in that
    brave old land—
  A safe and a pleasant lodging ;
No bailiffs are there ; there are no
    complaints
  Of the tenant his landlord dodging.

'Tis a fine old land of Democracy ;
  And wont it be wond'rous pleasant.
When the lord and the slave as equals
    meet,
  And the king's but the peer of the
    peasant !
How snugly I'll lie, with the clay
    packed down,
  And the blanket of sods above me,
With the rats at my feet, and the
    worms at my head,
  And along with me all who love
    me !
Change the tune !
And I'll prepare to greet you there,
  Almantha, when you come ;
I'll stand at the gate of the silent
    land,
  And sigh you a welcome home.
I'll twine thee a bower of mould'ring
    bones,
  Of faded hopes and fears ;
A well-scrubbed skull shall our
    goblet be,
  And for wine we'll have cold tears.
Our bower of gloom, in that land of
    peace,

Shall be tap'stried with sighs and
    moans ;
And we'll lightly waltz through the
    charnel halls,
  To the music of rattling bones.
The monarch who reigns in that land,
    my dear,
  Is jovial old King Death ;
He flings disease from his fine old
    fist,
  And the mildew's in his breath.
He sits on a throne of throbless
    hearts,
  Despair for his gentle queen ;
On his stately brow is the crown,
    " *Too late* ;"
  On hers is " *Might have been*."
" Ho ! ho !" he cries, with a gay
    guffaw,
  " I love the fair and good ;
The case that covers the richest soul
  Is still my fav'rite food.
I love to seize on the young and fair,
  To make the healthy bow,
And throw the veil of my viewless
    land
  Across the sweetest brow.
I love to seize on a maiden bright,
  To suck her cheeks soft bloom,
To drink the soul-light from her eyes,
  And fold her in the tomb.
I touch the captive ; his chains are
    dust :
  I touch the tortured heart,
And it writhes no more, and bleeds
    no more,
  When it feels my healing dart.
When every pant of the pulse is pain,
  And every heart-throb woe,
The only refuge for the wretch
  Is down with me below."
And oh, but *we'll* have the jovial time,
  Almantha, down below,   [night
In halls of gloom, and in glades of
  Where the streams of darkness
    flow—   [tears,
In the silent groves that drip with
  Each leaf a wasted heart,—   [wish
Hurrah ! the thought of it makes one
  To feel the cold sweet dart !
Hurrah, hurrah, for the dark old
    king !
Hurrah for the silent land !
Hurrah for the time when you and I

Flit into the breathless band!
Flit into the band—flit through the
     land—
One kiss, aud each away,
Duration digging his gulf of night
Between our shades for aye!
You'll go South to where winds of
     bliss
Over beds of rapture blow;
And I'll go North to enjoy myself
On eternal hills of snow.
You'll be mingled with all you love,
Nor hear my far-off moan

While I tread the wastes of Immensity
As I've trodden Life's—alone!
Away I through atoms of unborn
     worlds,
Through shipwrecked suns' debris;
Getting never away from Him, but
     still
Getting farther off from thee—
Away, away, through the wilds of
     Space,
To angel thoughts unknown—
The Wandering Jew of Eternity,
Alone, alone—and ON !

MY OWN OULD IRISH HOME.

Oh far-off fie'ls are butyful,
     An' far off cities fine,
An' far-off men are mighty nice,
     An' far-off girls—divine !
I've seen some places far away,
     But never let me roam
If any spot where I have been
     Is betther than ould home.
          For och it is a puity place,
               A dear ould place, a darlin'
                    place ;
          An' blissin's on its sonsy face—
               My own ould Irish home.
I've look'd ou splendid girls abroad
     With faces granly fine ;
But could they match the sweet, wee
     one
I here at home call mine?
They flash like sunshine on the eye
     An' give a sharp, short smart,
But this wee on' at home comes in
     An' lodges in the heart.
          For och, it's here's the winsome
               girl,
               The dear wee girl, the charmin'
                    girl,
          Love's softly-shinnin' darlin'
               pearl
               So sweetly set at home.
Then blessin's on the dear ould spot,
     An' blissin's on *her* be ;
For her or it, go where I will,
     No aiqual can I see,
An' ev'ry time that I'm away,
     No matther where I roam,
My heart grows lighter still as I
     Yet near to her and home
          For och, there's rapture in
               her face ;
          An', och, but its the darlin'
               place,
          If it could only get more pace—
               My own ould Irish home.

From Maglone's Letter to his
cousin Almantha of April 28,
1870. Parting Song to be
sung by Enniskillen when
she removes to a place in
Donegal bay, between Mul-
laghmore and Killybegs—
made by the Gran' Jury, an'
set to musick by Mr. Dan.
Petberson :—
Och, it's fare-you-well luvly Tyrken-
     nedy,
Fare-you-well Magheraboy,
My aushint an' loyal companyons
In many a sorrow an' joy.
You lov'd me so well that you choked
     me
While huggin' me many a year ;
But now I must try emmygration',
     An' part with my lovers, fareer !
The Water Committy declares it—
     The Chareman an' agent also—
An' likewise the cruel solicit-her
     Tells me that off I must go.
But, if I go I'll take with me
     Sir Lowry an' Tonystick still ;
An' throgs I'll not lave Neddy Nolan
     That sits on the hip of the hill.
Farewell to the hills an' the hollows,
     The fiel's, an' the valleys, an'
          sthrames ;
When I'm far away from Fermanagh,
     It's of them I'll think in my dhrames
Farewell to the Chrichtons an' Arch-
     dalls,
     To Loftus, Brooke, D'Arcy an'
          Maude,
To Bloomfield an' Barton an' Sankey,
     I'll think of them all when abroad.
A sollem farewell to the Porther
That's gardin' Fermanagh's ould gate
So well that that the de'il cannot pop in
His nose, tho' the watchman's so blate.

A SWINISH MATTER.

A poor man's pig was poisoned last winter in the County Fermanagh. The Grand Jury of that county lately held an inquest on the unfortunate deceased, but, as many of them thought the poison was placed about the country houses for the preservation of game, and that, consequently, the act of laying it was neither malicious nor wanton, they were unable to agree so far as to return a verdict. One of the " swinish multitude," moved, peradventure, by a fellow-feeling, had the impudence to perpetrate the following ballad-caoine—

The pig that lived at Belcoo, and died to save the game,
Immortal be the Memory of her dear grunting name ;
And if it's what she had no name while living in her pride,
We'll christen her the martyr Pig that for the game-law died.
Oh, weary on the day she went to take the frosty air,
And bitter sorrow on the hand that laid the poison there ;
May bother seize him, trouble plague him, scandal blight his name—
The murd'rer of the decent pig that died to save the game.
I'd lie awake a lee-long night to raise myself in time,
That, fresh and fasting, I might curse the baste that did the crime ;
Och ! may his spuds all take the blight, his flax forget to rot,
His turnips all grow up to stalks, his cabbage go to pot,
His hens refuse to lay an egg, his ducks refuse to quaick,
His honest cocks refuse to crow to make the rascal wake,
May all the music in his sowl be piggish grunts and squeels,
And till his death may Corrigan's dead sow be at his heels—
One sow ! Oh, let a mighty pack of angry pigs be there,
And to the gate of Fiddler's Green purshoo him like a hare.
And what about the jurymen, Fermanagh's crame and pride,
Who had no mercy on the pig that for the game-law died?
I pray and hope that they'll repent, amend their ways for shame,
And build a county monument to that poor martyr's name.
The lost one perished in their cause, 'twas for their sport she died ;
Her poor wee things are orphans for their pleasure and their pride.
But for their game-preserving ways she'd still be, wirresthrue !
A treasure to Patt Corrigan, a credit to Belcoo,
The guardian of her little ones, to watch their infant days,
And guide their growing grunting steps in decent piggish ways ;
Or, at the last and worst, she'd go to brander pan or pot,
Instead of lying where she lies in Bracken's field to rot.
Are sportsmen without gratitude ? and are the lost to shame ?
And will they not perpetuate their sinless victim's name—
The Martyr Pig of Corrigan, who died to save the game ?

TO IRELAND.

" Of all the lands the sun shines on
Old Ireland is the dearest one,
    Though not so grandly splendid,
To me earth's richest, sweetest grace
Is when the tears upon her face
    Are with her bright smiles blended.
" The grief that has been hers for years
Upon her wasted cheek appears,
    And in her eye-drop trembles,
But still behind that tear there's fun--
Behind that look, O darling one !
    A love that ne'er disembles.
" The storms of years have o'er thee
    passed
The night of ages been o'ercast.
    O blue-eyed child of sorrow !
But Erin, Erin, *tir mochree,*
    Duration is in debt to thee,
    And owes thee a bright morrow.
" 'Twill come, *agra*—'twill dawn,
    aroon—
The daylight will be on thee soon ;
But after that the full, high noon
    Bright o'er thy sky careering.
In that proud noon, beloved isle,
Thy children's bounding souls shall
    smile,
And sing ' Hurrah ! hurrah ! hurrah !
    Ar dochas agus Erin !'"
        * Hurrah for hope and Ireland.

MAGLONE'S HALLOWEVE COMPLIMENT.

Musha, Barney, its raly to bad
      Bedad,
To see the're lookin' so sad,
        My lad.
It's now Halloweve
An' you sit there an' grieve
On account of your sittin', like stone.
Poor, dismal pilgarlic. Maglone.

Other people have homes of their own,
      Maglone;
But your share of the worl's to have
    none,
      Movrone!
As you liv'd, you must die,
An' your last gasp or cry
Will be heard very likely by none,
      Not one—
You misfortunate divel, Maglone!

You're only a sthray among men,
      Again;
You'll never have chicken or hen;
      So, then,
You may growl at your aise;
You may die when you plaise,
Like a poor crippled bear in his den,
      My fren,
An the worl' be well shut of Maglone.

An' when they have laid down your
    head,
      When dead,

An' a quilt of green scraids on your
    bed
      Have spread,
Twill be comfort, d'ye mind,
To lave no one behind
To gulp fo· the spirit that's fled,
      Or shed
A tear on the sod of Maglone.

Though you ne'er had a Halloweve
    faste,
      At laste
You'll give the poor worms a taste,
      You baste!
Let them work as they will,
Let them feed their sweet fill,
Till they nibble you down in prime
    haste,
      Nor waste
A morsel of Barney Maglone.

An' when they have pick'd every bone,
      Ochone!
As smooth an' as bare as a hone,
      Maglone,
An' have empy'd the skull
That of nonsense was full,
They'll say " Come, boys, it's time to
    be gone,
      Come on —
He was mighty poor pickin',
    Maglone!"

THE LAKE OF THE BOWERY ISLES.

Let others sing the ocean,
  So wide, wild, and bounding free;
But mine be home emotion—
  Loch Erne of the isles for me.

In all its wayward changes,
  Its frowns and its sunny smiles,
My heart from it ne'er ranges—
  Loch Erne of the lovely isles.

From childhood I have loved it,
  And watched every shifting mood—
When stormy Winter moved it,
  When Spring sported on its flood.

When Summer came to woo it,
  And Autumn, with sober smiles,
Came stealing gently to it—
  Loch Erne of the verdant isles.

Oh let my steps ne'er wander,
  Save briefly from its blest shore,
Of which I aye grow fonder,
  And cling to it more and more.

I love it in its wild mood,
  I feast on its sportive smiles,
Companion of my childhood—
  Loch Erne of the bow'ry isles.

My infant breath was blended
  With breezes that swept its breast;
Here let my days be ended,
  And close to it be my rest.

It then shall still breathe o'er me,
  I then, too, shall share its smiles
With those who slept before me,
  The old saints of Erne's isles.

BELMORE STREET BAKERY.

M. FRITH,

GROCER, BAKER, & CONFECTIONER,

BELMORE STREET,

ENNISKILLEN.

COME and SEE the incomparable GOOD
VALUE in all kinds of

WOOLLEN DRAPERY GOODS,

Suitable for Ladies' and Gentlemen's Outfits, at

FOSTER & ANDERSON'S
LISNASKEA.

The most FASHIONABLE and DURABLE ARTICLES
in every DEPARTMENT, having numerous Customers
from beyond the LARGER TOWNS around ; far-famed
for being the CHEAPEST HOUSE in the TRADE, and
Selling at the LOWEST PRICE POSSIBLE for CASH.

ON THE ERNE.

JOHNSTON'S HOTEL,

BELLEEK.

ESTABLISHED OVER A CENTURY.

Has been entirely rebuilt on a site commanding a magnificent view of the Falls, the River, and the Old Bridge ; and the Donegal Highlands in the rere.

It will be found replete with every
Modern Comfort,

ON MODERATE TERMS.

D. Johnston, Proprietor.

"The Lisbellaw Gazette,"

OFFICE—LISBELLAW,

County Fermanagh.

LOCAL LIBERAL PUBLICATION,

Allied to no Clique or Faction.

Ventilates the needs of the North of Ireland ; with special reference to Agricultural Interests.

Appears on FIRST and THIRD TUESDAYS IN EACH MONTH.

SINGLE COPY, 1d. ; By Post, 1½d. One Year—Prepaid, 3s. ; Six Months—Prepaid, 1s. 6d.

ANDREW LAW,

25 High Street,

ENNISKILLEN,

Watchmaker,

JEWELLER, &c.

REPAIRS

Carefully and promptly executed on the Premises,
by First-Class Workmen.

Contracts taken for Winding and keeping Clocks in
Repair by the Year.

Eureka Neutral Tinted SPECTACLES for Im
proving and Preserving the Sight, always in Stock.

AGENT FOR THE

National Assurance Company of Ireland.

F. Little & T. Mulligan.

THE SLAUGHTER YARD

At the foot of

WATER STREET,

ENNISKILLEN.

Open every day during the Pork Season for the
purpose of KILLING PIGS,

Charge for Killing—

THREE PENCE PER PIG.

FRANCIS LITTLE,

HIDE MERCHANT,

WATER STREET,

ENNISKILLEN.

Hides of all classes and Wool purchased at the
best market prices.

Large quantities of Hides exported weekly to the
English and Scotch Markets.

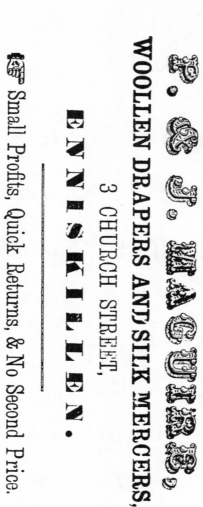

HENRY PIERCE,

PLASTERER,

AND

SLATER,

MILL STREET,

ENNISKILLEN.

CENTRE FLOWERS and TRUSSES
in variety.

JOHN SHANNON,

WINE

AND

SPIRIT MERCHANT,

24 Belmore Street,

ENNISKILLEN.

Guiness's Porter, &c., in Wood and Bottle.

Post Cars and Stabling.

LODGINGS, &c.

COMMERCIAL HOTEL,

DERRYGONNELLY,

MRS. TIMMONY,

PROPRIETOR.

FIRST - CLASS ACCOMMODATION.

POSTING in all its Branches.

A Two-Horse Van leaves the Hotel for Enniskillen on Tuesdays, Thursdays, and Fair Days.

JOSEPH TICKLE,

PLUMBER, GAS FITTER,

AND

HYDRAULIC ENGINEER,

6 & 7 Belmore Street,

ENNISKILLEN.

All kinds of Plumbing Work done in the best style and on the shortest notice,

Force and Lift Pumps,

Baths, Water Closets, Gas Fittings,

Lead and Iron Pipes.

JOHN WRAY,

CIVIL ENGINEER,

VALUATOR,

Land and Building

SURVEYOR,

HIGH STREET,

ENNISKILLEN.

1880.

THE WEIGHT-CARRYING SIRE,

"YOUNG WARDEN"

The Property of Mr ARCHIBALD NOBLE,

WILL STAND THIS SEASON

AT GLASSDRUMMOND.

Breeders should look out early as the horse will be let only to a limited number of Mares this Season.

Glassdrummond is One Mile from Lisnaskea, Two from Maguiresbridge, Nine from Enniskillen, Eight from Clones, Eight from Fivemiletown, Three from Brookeborough, and Seven from Tempo.

"YOUNG WARDEN" will attend the neighbouring towns on Fair Days.

TERMS — Gentlemen's Mares, £1 10s. and 5s. Groom's Fees. Farmer's Mares, £1 2s. 6d. and 2s. 6d. Groom's Fees. Groom's Fees to be paid at First Service. Service Money to be paid before 1st November, or 5s. extra will be charged.

Any Mare not proving in foal may have the Service of the Horse next season, by paying Groom's Fees, providing the Horse and Mare be in the present owners' possession.

"YOUNG WARDEN" when a Foal with his dam obtained First Prize at the Fermanagh Farming Society Show in Enniskilllen, and was awarded the Silver Medal at Lisnaskea Cattle Show, for the last three years.

"YOUNG WARDEN" is a beautiful rich brown; stands 16 hands high. with strong legs, deep body, short back, and powerful hind quarters; his formation combining that of the Race Horse and Weight-carrying Hunter, and is perfectly sound.

"YOUNG WARDEN" got by Old Warden, by the Hermit out of Blush (sister to Whim, the dam of Chanticleer), Blush by Blacklock, grandam Kiss, by Waxy Pope; her dam (Thetis' dam) by Champion, son of Pot-8-O's, winner of Derby and Leiger. The Hermit (one of the fastest horses ever trained in Ireland) was got by Birdcatcher out of Recluse by Wanderer; grandam by Orville out of the famous Alexander Mare; Birdcatcher by Sir Hercules; dam Guiccioli, by Bob Booty; Sir Hercules by Whalebone out of Peri by Wanderer. In the Hermit (Sire of the Warden) we have exactly the same breeding as Mr. Irwin's famous Mickey Free, both being got by the renowned Birdcatcher, and their dam by Wanderer—thus uniting in the Warden a rare combination of the best blood in England and Ireland. This Sire is half-brother of Sweep, the winner of the Cavan Handicap, also of Fairy Hill, winner of the Fermanagh Hunt Race.

He is now in the most blooming health and condition, and free from any natural blemish. His dam took first prize at the Enniskillen and Lisnaskea Cattle Shows in the years 1872 and 1876; and his sister took first prizes at Enniskillen, Lisnaskea and Newtownbutler Shows in 1878.

This powerful Weight-carrying Sire is the class of horse best calculated to improve our breed of horses. so fast declining in this country.

Grass 1s. per night to the 1st August, when the season will close. Every care and attention given to Mares and Foals but no accountability for accidents. Oats and Bran, if required, at Market price. No permission for Mares on Sunday.

Glassdrummond, Lisnaskea, January, 1880.